THE
BEST
OF
UFFA

Flying Cloud, *the Flying Fifteen designed by Uffa.*

THE
BEST
OF
UFFA

Fifty immortal yacht
designs from Uffa Fox's
five famous volumes

Edited by Guy Cole

Foreword by
The Duke of Edinburgh

ADLARD COLES NAUTICAL
London

Publisher's Note

All the photographs of boats are by Beken of Cowes, except where noted. Some are the same as appeared in the original volumes, but the printing blocks had been long destroyed, so fresh prints were taken in 1978 from Kenneth Beken's negatives dating back to the nineteenth century. Other photographs are contemporary, but did not appear in Uffa's five books. The photographs of Uffa himself have been supplied by Tony Dixon.

At the end of almost every section are the Editor's notes, set in this typeface.

Published 1998 by Adlard Coles Nautical
an imprint of A & C Black (Publishers) Ltd
35 Bedford Row, London WC1R 4JH

Copyright © Anthony Dixon 1998

First published in 1978 by Nautical Publishing Company
in association with George G Harrap & Co Ltd

ISBN 0-7136-4987-9

A CIP catalogue record for this book is available from the British Library.

Printed and bound in Great Britain by Redwood Books, Trowbridge, Wiltshire.

Designers are more usually known for the publication of their own works. Uffa Fox was not usual in any sense of the term. He combined an almost poetic nature with a highly practical and original turn of mind. He was a very successful designer, but he also had the generosity of spirit to recognise talent in others. This selection from Uffa's five volumes of 'immortal designs' betrays his lively appreciation of every aspect of sailing craft, from their sheer grace, the form and line of their hulls, the sweep of their sails, down to the very details of their construction. He sees them with the knowledgeable eye of a designer and turns what he sees into lucid prose.

The design of racing yachts has undergone a transformation since Uffa's day. Gone are what might be described as the 'natural' materials of wood, hemp and canvas. In their place are aluminium and man-made fibres, and computer-aided design. The sheer strength of these new materials has allowed designers to do things that would have not been possible with the 'natural' materials. I am quite sure that Uffa would have looked at them with the same discerning and critical eye. He would surely have approved of many of the contemporary designs, but I am equally sure that he would have condemned some features which, though they may enhance speed, he would have considered un-seamanlike.

For those lucky enough to have seen some of the yachts featured in this book, it will bring back many memories. For those who knew Uffa, it will be a reminder of this unique character. For those who love sailing, eat your hearts out.

Philip

Contents

from Sail and Power 1936	*from Racing, Cruising and Design 1937*	*from Thoughts on Yachts and Yachting 1938*
Vailima II 92 *Bonnie Dundee 95*	*Helgoland 104* *Brambling 106* *Andrillot 110*	*Dyarchy 137* *Sheila II 141* *Selina King 144* *Askoy 147*
Roland von Bremen 87 *Spica 90*	*Latifa 113* *Ortac 116* *Zeearend 119* *Golden Eye 122*	*'Distance racing' 150*
Vema III 98 *Germania II 101*	*Lake One-Design 129* *Dragon 131* *International One-Design 132*	*Circe 151* *Bonito II 154* *Mayfly 155*
Brynhild 83	*Thunder 134*	*Thunder and Lightning 157*

Preface

Uffa Fox. The name Uffa, given to him by his mother, who came from Suffolk, conjures up a mystical Viking character, Uffa being a Norse sea king. One feels that with such a name Uffa would inevitably have been drawn by the lure of the sea.

And so it was, but Uffa also had the added ingredient of charisma, for he only had to walk into a room full of people for his presence to be felt, and he would quite literally take over the proceedings, whether business or pleasure. Add to that his roguish smile and outrageous sense of humour and he instantly disarmed his fiercest critics.

That said, however, he did not suffer fools gladly and his tongue could be savage. I remember in 1947, as a very young apprentice in Uffa's drawing office, a senior salesman from Guest, Keen and Nettlefolds, manufacturers of nuts, bolts and screws, coming in and demanding to see Uffa, as he owed them quite a lot of money. Uffa sat the salesman down on one of the drawing office seats and said to him, 'Now look son, I have a system for all of our creditors so that each one gets a fair crack of the whip. Every month I find out from my accountant how much I can afford to pay out, and then I put all the creditors' names into a hat with the amount

Uffa. Courtesy of Anthony Dixon.

of money I owe them. Then I draw the names out until the amount I can afford to pay is reached. The creditors left then have to wait until next month for another chance. So listen carefully, because if you keep on complaining your ruddy name won't even go into the hat.'

In 1949 Uffa met Prince Philip during Cowes Week. With Uffa's breezy smile and extrovert character they became firm friends which lasted throughout Uffa's lifetime.

Prince Philip was a first rate helmsman and with Uffa as crew, having local knowledge of tides and weather in the Solent, they won many races in the Flying Fifteen *Coweslip*, which had been presented to Prince Philip by the people of Cowes.

One particular Cowes week when Prince Philip was staying on the Royal Yacht *Britannia*, Uffa's French wife Yvonne insisted that I tidied up the drawing office during Uffa's absence. Uffa was most untidy in this respect, and drawings had found their way into every nook and cranny. After I had finished, under Yvonne's direction, there was hardly a plan to be seen. Uffa was furious when he came back but could do little about it. The next morning I was working in the office when the door suddenly flew open, Prince Philip came into the room, looked all round in disbelief, and then at me and said, 'So sorry, I must be in the wrong house.' He then went out and shut the door behind him. Uffa's untidiness was clearly legendary.

After Uffa died in 1972 his memorial service was held at the church of St Martin-in-the-Fields, Trafalgar Square, London. Attending to honour an

Uffa aboard Coweslip. *Courtesy of Anthony Dixon.*

old friend were their Royal Highnesses Prince Philip, Prince Charles and Princess Anne, the lesson being read by the then Prime Minister, the Right Honourable Edward Heath. The orchestra from the Royal Yacht *Britannia* was also there playing Uffa's favourite sea shanty *Spanish Ladies*. At the finish of his address on that occasion Sir Max Aiken said, 'We mourn for the Uffa whose mind touches our hearts. He was pure gold.'

The Best of Uffa is a cross section of Uffa's five memorable books published in the thirties and it is quite incredible to think how he managed to persuade top yacht designers of that period to have their plans published. I cannot believe that today any of the world's top designers would allow their designs to be published by a fellow designer/author. The books were, in effect, one man yachting annuals, reflecting the best designs in the world (mainly British and American) carried along with Uffa's pungent comment. His labour and energy must have been prodigious, in view of all his other activities. Then, it is clear, Uffa was at his prime: the books have become classics, always in demand yet long out of print. This collection of fifty craft was selected by Guy Cole, who knew Uffa well. His notes and comments have been thoughtfully added where appropriate.

One of the designs published here is *Stormy Weather*, by Olin Stephens. Uffa would frequently take out her plans and show me her graceful lines. I am sure he considered her the finest craft of her type during that era. I recommend all of the designs in this book to the reader, as each one has its

Uffa at his house in Cowes, before going to the yacht club ball. Courtesy of Anthony Dixon.

individual merits worthy of careful study.

The reissue of this book will be a great boon for all Uffa lovers to add to their collection, as well as for younger sailors for whom Uffa is now entering into the land of legend.

Uffa in his drawing room. Courtesy of Anthony Dixon.

Introduction

From 1934 through 1938 Uffa wrote five large volumes which were published annually. He did hundreds of drawings to illustrate them: lines of the hull, sail plans, accommodation plans, construction drawings. These are works of art. Where there was buttoned upholstery on the saloon settees, he drew every button with its surrounding rosette of creases. He shows not merely the outline of a stern-knee, but also the pattern of grain on wood. As well as being of immense interest to the student of naval architecture, these drawings are a delight to the layman with only limited technical knowledge. It seemed a pity that they should be lost to all save those lucky enough to own copies of the original books (long since out of print, though second hand copies circulate at a high price), so we have made a selection for this single book. As much as possible of Uffa's commentary on the designs is given, together with some brief notes bringing out points of interest.

What grace they had, these old yachts, with swinging sheerline and well matched overhang at bow and stern! Owners leaving the mooring to go ashore in the dinghy must have looked back at them with a special little glow of pride. Only something which is intrinsically beautiful can evoke such feelings. Unlike commercial craft, yachts have no reason for *not* being beautiful. Their sole purpose is to give pleasure to the owner. Why make them ugly? The hulls depicted here partake of the natural harmony of Nature's own creations. Their flowing lines suggest the curl of a wave and the sweep of the wind blowing over the waters. Few things made by man achieve such aesthetic charm as this, the essential "rightness" of a Nash terrace, or a Chippendale chair, ageless in its appeal.

The finish of each hull was mostly white, or very occasionally black. There was a little gilding around the name on the stern, a gold cove-stripe running along just below the deck-line, ending with the merest suggestion of a flourish at the bow. The wood fittings around the deck, and the spars, had received coat after coat of varnish, giving them a deep gloss. The whole had a sort of restrained elegance like a Savile Row suit.

Modern readers browsing through the accommodation plans will be amazed by the paucity of berths on a given overall length. Our fathers liked some space around them. The close-coupled squalor of four bunks in a twenty-footer would have been considered appalling. The forward position of the galley on many of the yachts shown here was a lingering hang-over from paid hands who lived forward. It took the large all amateur crews of ocean racing to push the galley back abaft the saloon where the motion was so much easier. However, it should be remembered that the motion forward was by no means as violent in a vessel perhaps 60 ft. over all.

A feature of many of these accommodation plans, right down to 30 ft. is the "Fo'c'sle". The head was usually installed there, with plenty of elbow room all around it. There was a paint locker for all those half-filled tins of paint and varnish inseparable from maintenance of a wooden hull—and a sail-rack like a horse's manger. On one side was a pipe-cot for the extra unexpected guest in harbour, and when lashed back against the ship's side it formed convenient stowage for those long awkwardly-shaped articles difficult to stow elsewhere. But perhaps the greatest advantage of the fo'c'sle became apparent during an emergency sail-change at sea, when a wet headsail could be stuffed down through the fore hatch without harming anything, for the whole space there was a sort of "wet area".

Centuries of folklore lay behind the construction of these wooden hulls. They grew up on the floor of the building shed as naturally as a tree grows. First the keel was laid, and the stem and stern reared up from it, then the ribs, until the skeleton shape took on finality of line. This was clothed with planking, extending down from the gunwale and up around the turn of the bilge until the "shutter" was put in completing it. Next the caulker with his curiously-shaped hammer and long dangling strands of cotton. The painters with primer, undercoat and topcoat, until highlights glistened on the curves of the hull. It all followed a well-ordered sequence which could not be altered. So the yacht took shape on the water's edge, in the environment where she would spend her days.

Yacht yard foremen had spent a lifetime acquiring the lore of timber, in all its vagaries. They could go into the different species of African Mahogany called after various rivers. They knew the characteristics of different timbers in their old age, and when they had been insufficiently seasoned. They understood the effect of acids in the wood on metal fastenings, which might induce "nail-sickness". They could tell whether "shakes" in the spar were harmless or otherwise. They could feel imperfections in a surface with their finger-tips and smell the first tell-tale odour of rot.

Atop many of these ocean racing hulls is a Bermudian yawl rig. It was bred of the rules then in force which presented the mizen stay-sail "free"; but it sat quite prettily on the hull, and in hard weather with the main-sail reefed and only a stay-sail set forward the boats could be made very snug. Sails were of canvas and called for very precise judgement by the sailmakers in how far they would stretch along luff and foot, particularly racing sails which had to measure to the black band. Yachts were handled with great delicacy, in light breezes, when sails were new, a process known as "sail-stretching". In extreme old age, especially on cruising yachts, cotton sails could be tanned to give them further life.

The nineteen-thirties formed an interesting decade in yachting. At the outset deep-water men were still firmly tied to a straight stem and a long keel, with deep bulwarks and the rugged construction of the workboat, pilot cutters and sailing trawlers, and a heavily sparred gaff rig to top it off. Gradually, ocean racing taught the lesson that there was a different kind of seaworthiness, as well as that of the heavy boat which would just lie down and "take it". Bermudian rig was some time establishing itself among deep water men. It was insufficiently stayed at first, and this caused trouble. The way in which boats carried on racing in weather when all cruising yachts still at sea were hove to finally brought acceptance. Masts of cutters and sloops were moved further aft into the boat, shortened a little, and the staying improved.

In the thirties, Uffa Fox was somewhat of an "enfant terrible" among the "established" yachting circles. He held that weight was only of value in a steam-roller. When his theories were disparaged he had a habit of going out and performing some audacious feat of seamanship which proved him right. This was particularly so in his exposition of extreme light displacement for serious long distance seagoing. When he made a voyage in an older heavier craft, though, he was ever ready to pay his respects to their good qualities. Predilections Uffa may have had; but not sufficient to cloud the whole of his judgement.

One of Uffa's great precepts was: "The best ocean racer makes the best cruiser". I think I know what he meant. It is almost always more fun to sail a fast boat than a slow one, and yachts which continue racing in heavy conditions must be of the right breed. The winches and gadgets which enabled the big racing crews to continue to drive them in hard going also aided a couple of men nursing them along while merely cruising. Above all, they were designed to be lived in at sea, so that morale and efficiency could be maintained, all equally desirable in a cruiser. Sailed short-handed, with an early and drastic reduction of sail area in strong winds, they would be the more comfortable. It is always reassuring to know that you are in a boat which can cope with any weather which comes. Perhaps the greatest safety factor of all is the ability to make to windward in thoroughly bad conditions so as to keep off a lee shore. Danger lies close inshore among the rocks and shoals, not in deep water.

A considerable part of this volume is given over to pure cruising yachts, built as such, and for no other purpose. Some are modelled on traditional types. There are dangers in following these too slavishly. Many fishing smacks had low freeboard aft for convenience in working the nets, an undesirable feature in a cruising yacht. Other designs given in this section are of notable ships, either by reason of what they achieved, or because they were outstanding examples of their type. There is the "dreamship", built for an owner who knew just what he wanted, and one or two motor-sailers.

In another there are examples of boats to the International (IYRU) Rule, the "Sixes", "Eights", and "Twelves". They had a classic grace which was all their own. We give, too, an example of the lordly "J"'s used in the pre-war America's Cup contests, and the svelte "Square Metre" classes rated on sail area.

Browse, then, through these pages of old designs, pausing where you will. Amid all the froth and nonsense of rating and rules, the clashing theories, two factors remain constant: the forces of wind and wave. These have been with us since time began; and the tides and currents, and their interaction with the wind. Somewhere there must lie a "perfect shape" for a yacht—one yielding maximum speed at all wind strengths, with windward ability to claw off a lee shore, able to care for the crew in the ultimate storm, and beautiful, too. Perhaps this paragon is just as likely to be found in the past, as in the present, or the future?

Uffa Fox

His parents chose more wisely than they knew, when they called him after the old Norse Sea King "Uffa",* or did he spend the rest of his life trying to live up to that name?

He was born in 1898 in the Isle of Wight, grew up on the Cowes waterfront, and taught himself to swim in the waters of its Medina River. His school was two miles distant, four miles to walk there and back, and I dare say this helped to take some of the steam out of him! In those far-off days, before World War One, there were oil lamps and a candle to go to bed with. Horse-drawn vehicles were the normal means of transport, or the steam railway for longer journeys. For entertainment, they gathered around the piano and had a sing-song, then each in turn performed his or her "party piece", and if the performance was sometimes excruciating at least that was good for a laugh afterwards. At his mother's urging he became a choir boy, an avocation which may surprise those who only knew the later Uffa; many years later coming in on the last leg of a "Round-the-Island" race, a great roaring chorus of "Onward Christian Soldiers" came drifting across to us from Uffa's boat.

When school-days were over he began an apprenticeship with S. E. Saunders, boatbuilder. Even then they were engaged with high speed craft like *Maple Leaf IV*, which made over fifty knots and hulls for the earliest flying-boats. Work started at six in the morning, and finished at half past five. In the war it was a "reserved" occupation, but through a mistake Uffa received calling up papers and immediately joined the Royal Naval Air Service. The youthful Uffa had dreamed of flying through the air and shooting down the enemy; but, as many another man has found in the Forces, he was put to the job where he would be most useful. That was servicing and repair of flying boats, including some he had actually helped to build himself, at S. E. Saunders! The Royal Naval Air Service had merged with the Royal Flying Corps to become the new Royal Air Force by the time Uffa landed back in civilian life.

He had been one of the earliest recruits to the Cowes Sea Scouts and worked his way up through King's Scout, Assistant Scout Master and then Scout Master. Their favourite craft was the old *Valhalla*'s whale-boat, thirty-two feet long, entirely open, fine lined for easy rowing and carrying a dipping lug. In her they ranged the English Channel from Brighton to Brixham and crossed over to Le Havre and made their way up the Seine to Meulan, thirty miles from Paris. On the return from this trip, having sailed through the night and the following day, they beached the boat at nightfall on the southern shore of the Island. Two of the Scouts then walked barefoot fifteen miles over the downs to Cowes so as not to be late for work in the morning.

Including six months at the Thames Iron-Works building steam ships for the British India line, Uffa's apprenticeship had lasted seven years. It covered boat building, shipbuilding and design, as he intended to become a naval architect. At the age of twenty-one he set up his own boat building business. His father arranged for the deeds of certain properties willed to him to be deposited in the bank against an overdraft and introduced him to timber merchants and other suppliers. Uffa now acquired the old super-annuated steam driven "floating bridge", a flat ferry vessel, which had linked East and West Cowes. It was of Lomore iron, almost indestructible and therefore everlasting. He moved it up-river and the central part for horse-drawn carriages and the earlier motor-cars was roofed over to form a workshop. The prow at one end formed a gangway to the shore and the other became a slipway for launching boats into the river. The appendages along either side, forming cabins for foot passengers and a housing for the steam engine and its boiler, were converted to a drawing office and living accommodation. The tanks for water to supply the boiler, when cleaned and cement washed, furnished a domestic water supply. The six foot depth within the hull was storage space.

The Income Tax Authorities slapped a Property Tax on him. After much correspondence the Income Tax Inspector at Arreton, in whose parish of Whippingham the floating bridge was moored, summoned him to appear at court. It so happened that four parish boundaries met in that part of the river. They had some urgent work on in boat sheds further down and with the aid of an Easterly wind and a four-oared gig manned by boat builders moved the floating bridge down there, passing through three other parishes en route. Uffa then wrote to the Tax Inspector asking by what right he sought to collect Property Tax in East Cowes and that furthermore the floating bridge had been in the parishes of Northwood and West Cowes, as well as Whippingham, during the period in question. I would have given

If not addressed or discussed as "Uffa", then it was "Uffa Fox"; no one ever spoke of "Mr Fox"!

much to see the expression on that Tax Inspector's face when he found the "property" to be in East Cowes! After it had all blown over the floating bridge was quietly put back in its original berth.

Uffa's first Atlantic crossing had been in *Typhoon*, 45 feet long, and owned by Bill Nutting, Editor of the American magazine *Motor Boat.* Though ostensibly a cruising ketch, she had a hollow bow and a broad stern like a motor boat and the crossing was not without its traumas. They had one knock-down where the masts were way below the horizontal. The inside ballast shifted and burst up through the floor boards to lodge in the corner of the coach-roof, mixed with ashes from the stove, which proved that they had been very nearly upside down. It must have given Uffa something to think about in his designing! The next Atlantic crossing was in *Diablesse*, a fine schooner—with Bobby Somerset as navigator.

Uffa Fox in about 1930, possibly at Cowes railway station on return from a cruise.

On board Vigilant *(see page 41). Original caption: A small vessel must not load herself with useless gear, so the sextant mirror was used for shaving.*

He also did the 1931 trans-Atlantic as one of the crew on *Landfall*, a 71 ft. ketch designed by L. Francis Herreshoff, being especially responsible for sail trimming. The boat building business in the Isle of Wight was so arranged that it ran itself during these long absences. The chief draughtsman took over, and, if he was away, the foreman boatbuilder, then the foreman fitter, and so on.

Uffa was the father of the planing dinghy. Up till then all racing dinghies had merely heeled over and ploughed through the water. Having worked on high speed power craft during his apprenticeship, Uffa believed that if a dinghy hull were made the right shape, and her crew held her bolt upright, she could be made to plane over the surface. He was a little diffident about it; but finally gave these theories full rein in the Fourteen Foot International *Avenger*. In 57 starts she got

52 Firsts, 2 Seconds and 3 Thirds. After twenty wins on the trot in the Solent they loaded her with 3 cwt. of water, food, clothes, compass, charts and gear and three of them sailed her across to Le Havre. They won two races in France and then sailed back, tacking into a head wind all the way, and Uffa doing mental arithmetic calculating the strain on the weather shroud. All modern planing dinghies stem from this beginning.

Among the craft Uffa owned in his earlier years was a steam launch. Like everyone else, he found the smooth silent power of steam fascinating. Wildfowling in the Newtown creeks they found that, provided there was a little breeze to keep the birds head to wind, they could glide right up to them. Another of his earlier loves was the twenty-ton schooner *Black Rose*—built in Stornaway to carry passengers and freight to the Western Isles. With her clipper bow, long bowsprit, and a

This was used as the frontispiece in the Second Book (1935).
Original caption: The author at work on the design of
Wishbone.

chequered row of black-and-white squares like
gun-ports along her topsides, she had a rakish
piratical air. She, too, was sometimes used for
wildfowling, including a boozy, hilarious, mid-
winter expedition to the Lymington marshes
when Uffa fell into the icy water, but pressed on
with the duck-shoot anyhow. Uffa for a time was
stroke in a four-oared gig which they rowed up
and down the Solent to various regattas, and they
also did the fifty-five mile trip round the Island.
After cabling a challenge to America, he designed
two canoes, *Valiant* and *East Anglian*, to conform
to both the British and American rules, and built
them in his own yard. These canoes were sailed
by one man using a sliding-seat and could
achieve a speed of 16 knots. Uffa and Roger De
Quincey shipped *Valiant* and *East Anglian* to
America, raced among the Thousand Islands of
the St. Lawrence River, and on Long Island
Sound, and brought back the International Canoe
Trophy and a lot of other cups as well.

After the floating bridge, Uffa lived at Twenty
Acres, a house standing in that much ground
beside the Medina River. He designed it himself
and lined it up by compass to face south for the
maximum amount of sun. (I envy him that, for I
have always longed to be able to do it.) Still
scorning electricity and piped water, he made the
place entirely self-sufficient. Then the authorities
wanted to run an overhead power cable on
pylons across his land. It so happened that Uffa
had designed two smaller houses for domestic
staff, well away from his own. These plans were
already passed and approved, he produced them
at the appropriate moment, and the power cable
had to be put underground—greatly to the
benefit of the scenery.

Uffa was always ready to prove his theories
correct with a practical demonstration. *Vigilant*
was such an extreme example of light displacement that the "Q" Class refused to allow her to
race with them in the Solent, yet he sailed her to
Sweden and back in a summer of strong winds.
He made many friends in the Baltic countries and
did a lecture tour there one winter. Very different
to the *Vigilant* trip was the voyage from Norway
to Cowes in the Falmouth Quay Punt *Twilight*,
finding out how this heavy-displacement type
behaved while running down across the North
Sea in a series of northerly gales. Six Metres were
invariably treated as day boats; but Uffa, who
could always be relied on to do the unexpected,
sailed *Lintie* from Cowes to the Whitaker Beacon,
at the mouth of the River Crouch, in 21 hours. His
experience in every kind of craft was as wide as
can well be imagined, and this was invaluable, for
a designer.

To accommodate his expanding business Uffa
bought the Medina Yard in West Cowes on the

other side of the river. The premises were old, deriving from a big house called Birmingham Hall, once occupied by Thomas Arnold the famous Headmaster of Rugby School. Many alterations and improvements were made. Eventually, Uffa had a compact and easily run yard where the timber flowed in at the sawmills and passed through the various boat shops until the completed craft could be launched into the river. When he first set himself up in business Uffa told the local Secretary of the Shipwrights' Union he would employ only first-class boatbuilders and would pay them above Union and Port rates. If the Union ever came to his Works to tell him how to treat men, it would mean he was not fit to employ them, and he would release them all to the Union. At Medina Yard Uffa still "lived over the shop". His drawing office, the firm's offices, and his living accommodation were all contained in Medina House, adjacent to the yard. Later, this was partly destroyed by enemy bombing.

People had grown accustomed to Uffa's eccentricities; but some eyebrows were raised when he took off across the Channel in a two-man sliding-seat canoe. *Brynhild* made the crossing from the Needles to Cherbourg in twelve hours, averaging seven knots. Then Uffa and Bill Waight, his chief draughtsman, cruised the North Brittany coast out to the west, rock-dodging close inshore most of the time, and camping on the beach at night. It was proof of what could be accomplished in such a frail craft. In those days few had attempted anything of this sort and it was audacious.

Air Commodore Burling was in charge of flying boats stationed at Mountbatten, Plymouth. Uffa designed and built for him an 18 ft. Jolly Boat which could be carried under the wing of one of the great machines down to his home in the Scilly isles and back to Plymouth. When war came again, in 1939, crews of our aircraft which had been forced to "ditch" were left sitting in their rubber dinghies waiting to be rescued. Uffa conceived the idea of the Airborne Lifeboat, carried underneath the aeroplane and parachuted down to the survivors, a seaworthy craft in which they could get back to England. Lord Brabazon, a sailing man and a friend of Uffa's, was Minister for Aircraft Production and he gave the scheme his blessing.

Lightly built, with lines which blended with the streamlined shape of the aeroplane, the Airbornes had sails, an engine, and were full of survival kit, including instructions on how to sail! The Mark II, 30 ft in length, had a cruising range under power of 500 miles, later increased to 1,000 miles. When the big Flying Fortresses did daylight raids on enemy territory, and got riddled with shot, they often crashed into the sea near Heligoland on the way back. Many of their U.S. Air Force crews were rescued with Airbornes. At one time it was intended that a Coxswain should be dropped with the boat; but the dummy man used in trials got decapitated and it was never done. The navigator and pilot of a Mosquito which "ditched" in the Bay of Biscay got back to the Scillies in an Airborne parachuted down to them. There were plans for a fifty-footer to carry over two hundred men for use in the Pacific War; but the atom bomb brought it to a swift conclusion, so they were never needed.

For nine years Uffa lived in the big house at Puckaster, on the southern shore of the Isle of Wight. A little cove there offers smooth water

Uffa's letter head.

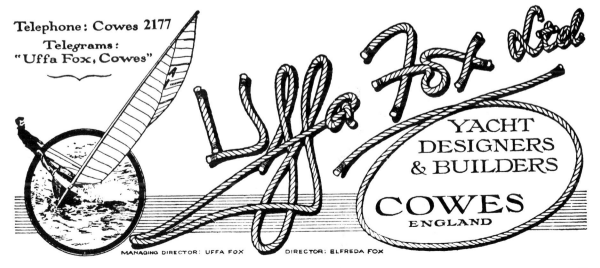

Telephone: Cowes 2177
Telegrams:
"Uffa Fox, Cowes"

Uffa Fox Ltd

YACHT
DESIGNERS
& BUILDERS
COWES
ENGLAND

MANAGING DIRECTOR: UFFA FOX   DIRECTOR: ELFREDA FOX

inside the fierce tidal race off the headland. The house itself was gabled and windowed in all directions. Uffa had a couple who served him as cook and butler and there were gardeners to tend the extensive grounds and gardens where generations of loving hands had planted cedars, orchards and walnut trees. Grapes and peaches flourished in the mild climate, where he could sometimes have breakfast out on the terrace in the first days of January. The house was built upon rock, with a well giving a supply of the clearest, purest drinking water imaginable. Uffa then converted the little farm cottage at Puckaster and used that as a country home for a further six years before he moved back into Cowes, as he planned to do, for his old age.

In World War 2 in Puckaster Cove, where Uffa kept one of the airborne life-boats ready in case a returning aircraft should ditch.

Immediately after the war he was closely associated with Fairey Marine, of Hamble, when they were building hot-moulded boats of his design. The hot-moulding process consisted of layers of thin veneers, glued, and then the whole hull baked in a large oven called an autoclave. The 12 feet Firefly was produced in great numbers. Another design was the 18 feet Jolly Boat which made 16 knots and beat all comers in the early speed trials at Cowes. *Fairey Fox* was a monster dinghy, 24 feet 6 inches, which they built for the Duke of Edinburgh. For this one Uffa reverted to a gunter rig, though he modernized it with a claw-ring at the masthead through which the head of

the gunter yard was rove, keeping it absolutely vertical.

Although he had been well known in yachting for many years, it was Uffa's association with Royalty which spilled his name over onto the broad mass of the British public. Stop the first man you met in the street with the question, "Who is Uffa Fox?" and he would rub his chin thoughtfully and answer: "Something to do with boats isn't he?" Not even the greatest names in yachting had ever attained that sort of eminence. He and the Duke raced together in the Dragon *Bluebottle.* The Prince of Wales, then quite a boy, often went along with them. The Royal helmsman, with Uffa as crew, was also prominent in Cowes Week racing with the Flying Fifteen *Coweslip.* This small keel boat, twenty feet in length, was one of Uffa's more successful post-war designs and has built up into a large class.

He served in the boating advice bureau at all the earlier London boat shows. I had a desk there, too. I have seen men come along the aisle looking glum—probably their feet ached from all the traipsing around. Then they sighted him sitting there. With an ecstatic shout of "Uffa!", faces cracked open in a tremendous grin, they darted forward with hand outstretched. I marvelled over a man who could have that kind of effect on people. An important visitor who had come from half across the world would enquire where he was. "That's his desk over there," I would say. "Do you know when he will be back?", glancing anxiously at a very expensive wrist-watch, "I have an appointment with him at two." I might have hazarded a guess at one or other of the "wet" stands, where Uffa was probably dug in with some of his cronies, but I forbore. He was so utterly unpredictable. After the distinguished visitor had shuffled around biting his fingernails for an hour, I might suggest he try the press room or the organizer's office, not in any anticipation of finding Uffa, but merely to give him something to do. Uffa was utterly bereft of all sense of time.

Most people think of Uffa only in connection with boats. This is an error. He had a .22 rifle when a boy and was seldom without a gun thereafter, for rabbits, and other rough-shooting, and wildfowling in the marshes. Neither was he ever without a dog. Having run in the Royal Air Force cross country team he was useful with the Isle of Wight Beagles. Cricket and football he played as a boy, and continued with cricket through much of his life. His favourite cricket match was the one played out in the middle of the Solent, when a small area of the Brambles bank uncovers at the equinoxial tides each September. There is not very much time before the tide returns, so there have to be special rules, like

As he became known to a wider public in the 1950s: Uffa on the Dragon Bluebottle, *with Prince Philip and young Prince Charles.*

hitting the ball into the water counting as six. It was the sort of boyish prank Uffa loved.

For twenty-five years the mare Frantic was his constant companion. From Puckaster he used to ride up across the downs to Arreton Manor to see his old friend Charlie Yeates. Having settled the mare down with oats and hay and water, he and Charlie would yarn over a little noggin, then dinner, port, more yarns, out to "sprinkle ammonia over the lawn", as Uffa called it, liqueurs, and out again for the benefit of the lawn. At two in the morning the mare was saddled up for the return and led to the old mounting block. Uffa swung his leg over and then tightened the girth after his weight was in the saddle, because she liked it that way. Charlie, holding her head, would say:

"All right, Uffa?"

"Yes, goodnight, Charlie."

Her head was loosed and she flew off down the drive like an arrow from a bow. The last Charlie saw of them was the sparks struck by her hooves from the flints. Through the moon-shadowed countryside they went, sometimes Uffa managed to slow her temporarily, then away again in a swift canter. Third member of the trio was Bruce, the Labrador, who always accompanied Uffa on these rides. Where branches of trees hung low he crouched over her withers, she took five-barred gates in her stride, they clattered through sleeping villages and past lonely farm-houses, until at last they came to Puckaster where dawn was stealing in from the English Channel.

Once, Uffa rode her through the front hall, up the stairs, and into his bedroom. Suddenly, he felt the floor trembling under their combined weight, and had a horrifying vision of her four feet sticking through the ceiling into the room beneath. Soberly, he slid off and gingerly backed her out and got her down the stairs. He was exploring an unknown part of the local terrain on Frantic when he found himself running out of path, with a sheer drop on the one hand and the towering cliff-face on the other. Fortunately, there was a close rapport between horse and rider. He slid outwards and downwards around her neck and under her head, then backed her for a hundred yards to where it was possible to turn round.

Uffa was married three times. His first wife Alma, played a big part in the preparation of the five big books. In 1941 he married Cherry and then in 1956 a French lady, Yvonne Bernard. He used to spend time in France, and had an office in Paris for a while. There was a very serious illness when he was cared for in the house of friends of his in the Midlands. From then on his activity was more intermittent. He had lived a very complete life, sparing himself not at all so long as every kind of activity could be entered into with zest.

The last residence was the Commodore's House, overlooking Cowes harbour, which has since been kept as a sort of Uffa Museum. It is a three-storey stone-built warehouse, three hundred years old, standing on the edge of the quay. With balconies added, and painted in gay colours, it has taken on rather an Italianate air. Designed specifically for his old age, it had a lift serving all three floors and the roof garden. As well as this, the stairs had a landing between each floor, providing a rest from climbing, and minimizing any accidental fall, and a continuous hand-rail from top to bottom exactly the right size to afford a good grip. During his lifetime Uffa had acquired many fine pieces of furniture and here it could all be displayed well. Much of it was old stuff; but often ingeniously employed in some quite modern usage. The size of the place permitted very large rooms, and they are all sumptuously appointed. The kitchen is enormous, and equipped with every kind of device, ancient and modern, to accord with Uffa's not always orthodox ideas about food.

The last boat Uffa designed was one for himself. It was a 25 feet launch, powered with two outboard motors, giving a speed of eighteen knots. She was built on the ground floor of Commodore's House and he called her *Ankle Deep*. He made fishing and picnic expeditions in her and, for instance, was in her at the start of a tall ships race in the summer of 1972, hailing his friends in the great mass of spectator boats.

He died in October of that year. There were memorial services both in London and at Trinity Church, Cowes, a sailors' landmark just alongside the Royal Yacht Squadron. Cowes in winter is not much frequented by sailors —only the locals are normally seen there —but on that winter day they packed the church for the short service at which Uffa's friend Max Aitken read the lesson. He will go on being remembered, not merely as a designer and sailor, but as a writer, philosopher and character for a wider world.

Sailing, Seamanship and Yacht Construction
and
Uffa Fox's Second Book

We have weekly and monthly periodicals devoted to yachting, but no Yachting Annual, and so the publisher and I thought it would be a good scheme to bring out a book every year, which would review each year's sailing, and place on record for all time examples of the best vessels of that year. This idea was stimulated by the gratifyingly widespread demand for my first volume, *Sailing, Seamanship and Yacht Construction*, which clearly indicated the fact that yachtsmen need such books. My *Second Book* therefore is the second volume of a series to which further volumes will be added every winter from now on.

When we sing or hum the tune which we have heard played by some wonderful orchestra, we seem to hear again the full orchestral symphony. In the same way, I sincerely hope that the words of this book will conjure up many happy memories of the sea, and that readers will hear the surge and swish of the bow cleaving the waters, the hum of the wind in the rigging and the taste of the brine in the mouth, and that it will bring to them the restful feeling that sunshine and sea air alone can bring.

As we go through life we find the simplest things give us the greatest pleasure. The silvery pathway on the water made by the moon, the black and silver of the clouds on a moonlight night—such things, when seen from the sailing ship, fill us with a joy that surpasses all others. Sailing will endure, because it is one of the few things left on this earth that bring a man close to nature in a natural way.

In my first book I included only designs of the fastest racers and best cruisers, and I have followed the same rule in this *Second Book*, the best designers in the world having generously given me their plans. Francis Herreshoff, Knud Reimers, Olin Stephens, Alfred Mylne, William Fife, Starling Burgess, Henry Gruber, W. J. Roue, have thus helped me, and all sailing men should be grateful to them, as I am myself, for allowing me to publish their latest and best work. These designers are so good that they can afford to give away their plans, knowing full well that they can do better another year.

from *Introduction* to the *Second Book*

Vamarie

Owner, Vadim Makaroff
Designers, Cox and Stevens

LOA 72 ft. 0 in.
LWL 54 ft. 0 in.
Beam 15 ft 3 in.
Draught 10 ft. 4 in.
Displacement 46 tons
Sail area 2,300 sq. ft.

In the autumn of 1933, as I sat writing in the cockpit of *Dorade* in Oyster Bay, a bright varnished ketch came roaring by under jib, mizen, and mizen staysail only, as the wind was strong. Her rig stood well, for a wishbone aloft held the two masts together, thus putting the strains fairly evenly over both spars, so that this vessel combined the handiness of the ketch with the strength of the schooner rig.

The rig was new to my eyes, and I wondered how it would stand in a strong wind and heavy sea. I was tempted then to ask her designers for her plans to publish in this book, but did not do so, for the rig was unproved and untried.

Months later, as I still sat writing this book, but now on the cliffs of Alum Bay in England, the news came through that *Vamarie* had, in a hard wet drive to windward, won the race from Miami to Nassau. During this race the wind blew 50 miles an hour, and caused nine out of the twelve starters to retire hurt. Sitting on the cliffs, and imagining her plunging and driving through the steep heavy seas caused by that wind, I at once decided that *Vamarie* was worth her salt and place in this book. Then cables flew to Rassmussen in Bremen and Jasper Morgan in New York, and soon

I was engaged in redrawing *Vamarie*'s lines, accommodation, sail, gaff and gaff fitting plans, and wondering why I had waited until she had proved herself so weatherly, when the impression she had made months ago told me she would be able and seaworthy.

The lines are those of an easily driven vessel, and there is no doubt that they make for a fast, well-balanced and weatherly hull.

The accommodation is unusually planned. The fo'c'sle has three cots, and directly abaft are the galley and pantry. Then there is a single guest cabin to port with a wash room opposite. Next is the saloon, which is very well lighted, even when the 14-foot dinghy is stowed on deck, for the coach roof is cut away on the starboard side to take the dinghy, and though it covers the starboard saloon lights those to port are clear. These are immediately over the saloon table where light is needed, and this unusual arrangement is a good one.

The companionway, as it is abreast the mast, is off centre on the starboard side, and opposite is another wash room, these two dividing the double cabin aft from the saloon. Further aft is a very fine navigator's cabin, where the chart table is built over the engine and so forms the engine casing. The companionway leading directly on deck to the wheel allows the navigator and helmsman to talk over the course, speed and weather without disturbing the rest of the ship: an admirable arrangement.

Unusual as are the details of her accommodation her sail plan is a new conception of the art of spreading canvas to catch the winds. Although the staysail and mizen are normal, the sails between the main and mizen masts are a new development. The mainsail is shaped like a topsail with a split gaff to extend the clew and

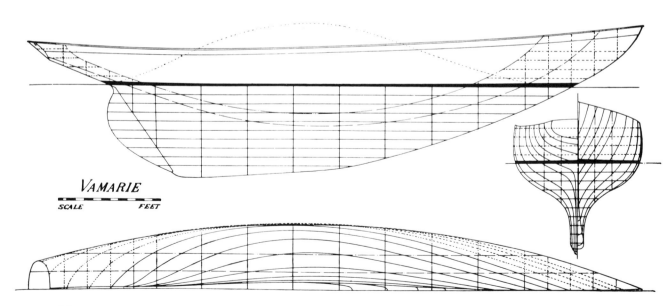

VAMARIE

SCALE   FEET

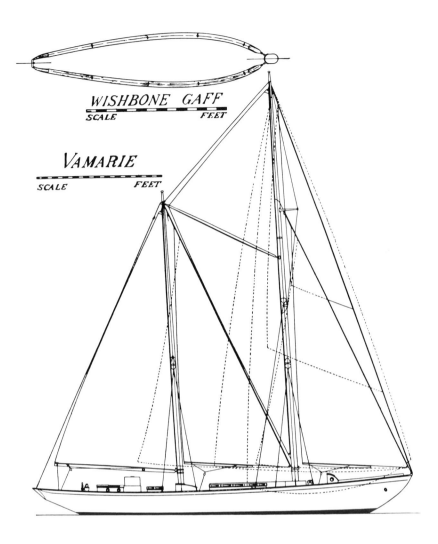

WISHBONE GAFF
SCALE   FEET

VAMARIE
SCALE   FEET

allow the sail to take its natural flow, so essential for windward work on either tack. The topsail usually found in gaff-rigged vessels takes a nice curve on one tack, and on the other, because it presses against the peak halyards, is perfectly flat, and so loses its power and drive to windward.

So the fact that a topsail is more efficient on the tack that blows it to leeward of the peak halyards, is generally the cause (unknown to some owners) of their vessels being faster on one tack. If there is a long and short leg to windward the really good skipper of a racer sets his topsail so that it bellies out to leeward on the long leg, and presses against the peak halyards on the short leg. Below *Vamarie*'s mainsail the mizen staysail is set, and tacks down on deck immediately abaft the mainmast, thus filling in the rest of the space between the two masts. With her unusual accommodation and sail plan, and her undoubted ability to windward under three lowers in severe weather, *Vamarie* is instructive and well worthy of study.

This looks like the beginning of Uffa's long love affair with wishbone rig, culminating in his designing the yacht called *Wishbone*. The rig is one of those terribly logical things which people enthuse over, wondering why all yachtsmen do not adopt it immediately. Yet it has never been popular—always confined to isolated examples. A big ketch like *Vamarie* was ideally suited to demonstrating its virtues; but there is always the pull of the wishbone sheet on the head of the mizen mast.

The Miami–Nassau Race is in two halves, the first part across the deep blue waters of the Gulf Stream and then threading the banks and shallows of the Bahamas. Both parts can be difficult in strong winds. Not until 1941 was the Southern Ocean Racing Conference started and the Miami–Nassau race included.

The navigator's cabin adjacent to the cockpit on *Vamarie* is excellent; but on a yacht 72 ft. over all there is room for such things!

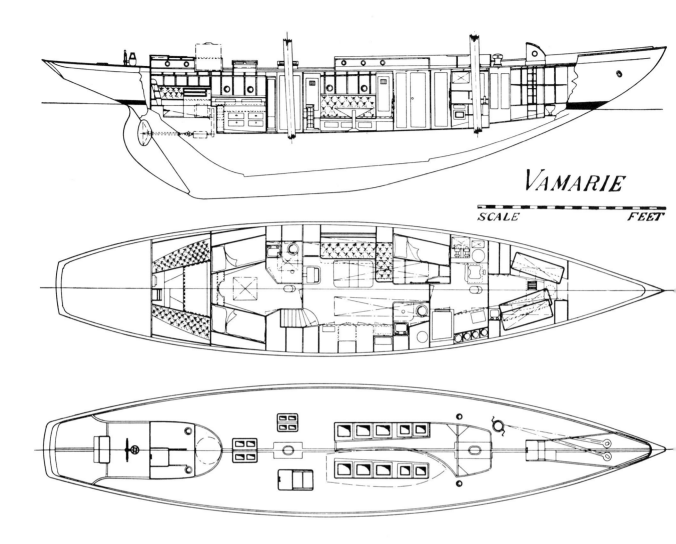

VAMARIE

SCALE   FEET

Niña

Owner and Skipper, Paul Hammond
Designer, Starling Burgess

LOA 59 ft. 0 in.
LWL 50 ft. 0 in.
Beam 14 ft. 10 in.
Displacement 40 tons
Sail area 2,500 sq. ft.

By winning the Transatlantic and the Fastnet Races in 1928, *Niña* proved herself a fast and able ocean racer. Her successful racing career no doubt influenced Vanderbilt to entrust Burgess with the designing of *Enterprise*, with which he successfully defended the America's Cup against *Shamrock V*.

Niña, anchored off Cowes, looked as strange to me as the *America* must have to our seamen in 1851, for both had rigs that were new to England. The *America*, it must be remembered, on August 22, 1851, won the

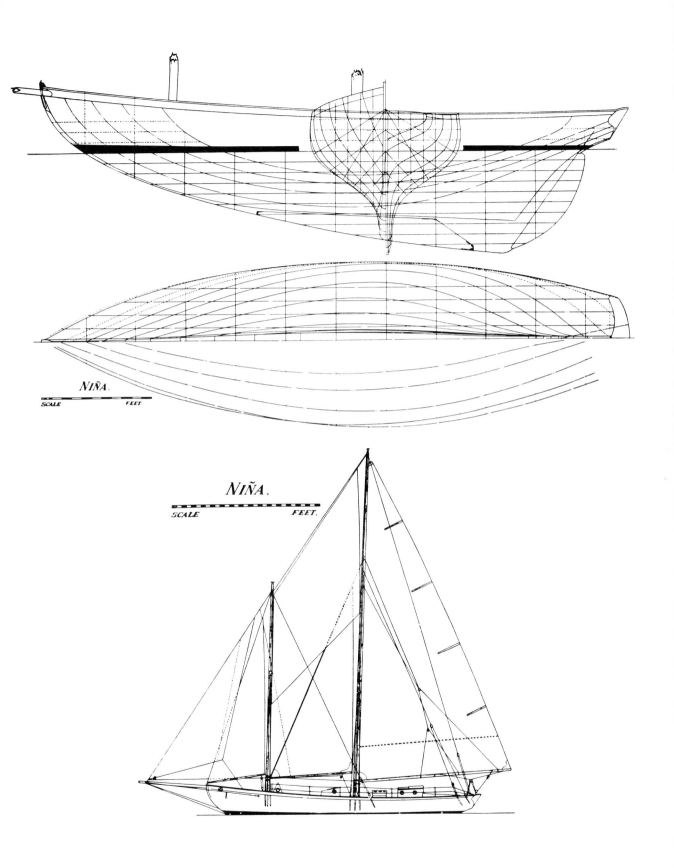

NIÑA.

SCALE FEET

NIÑA.

SCALE FEET

cup presented by the Squadron for a race round the Isle of Wight, six years later giving it to the New York Yacht Club, since when it has been known as the America's Cup.

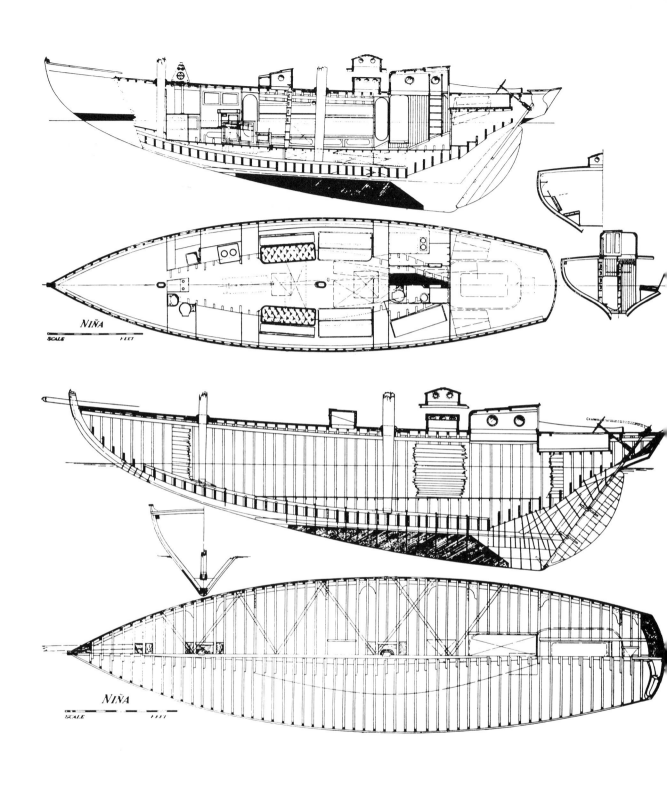

NIÑA

SCALE   FEET

NIÑA

SCALE   FEET

Before her visit, schooners in this country did not use the triatic stay (from mainmast head to foremast head above fore gaff), both masts being stayed independently of each other, which allowed the foretopsail to remain set when tacking. Besides introducing the triatic stay, America changed our

24

racing sails from flax to cotton.

Niña and *America* were alike in that they were both invading yachts with strange new rigs, both winning cups for America from England, thus putting these National cups on the higher plane of International cups.

Her short ends are the result of the American Ocean Racing Rule, otherwise it is certain *Niña* would have had longer overhangs fore and aft. The result would be a shorter bowsprit, would make reefing the mainsail easier, as well as giving stability, steadiness, and speed in a seaway.

Sweeping buttocks, easy diagonals, and waterlines, high, firm, yet not hard bilges, all combined make as sweet a set of lines as could be wished for. No wonder Burgess gave *Enterprise* the same sections and buttocks.

Niña's lines I've always admired (excepting the short ends), the hull hauled out and the model in the owner's home being pleasing to my eye. With her small amount of wetted surface she is easily driven, while the outside lead ballast enables her to stand up to hard weather.

The staysail schooner rig is quite new; *Advance* started it some six years ago in America. For windward work it is unquestionably faster than the ordinary schooner rig, and while it never can be as fast, it makes for an easier handled vessel than a cutter, with its sails split up into so many small pieces. In effect the rig is a cutter with small mainsail and a large fore triangle.

So as *Niña* at the best is a cutter with a small mainsail and a large foretriangle, she cannot expect to hold a similar hull with a cutter rig of normal proportions to windward, for besides the proportions of her headsail to mainsail being wrong for windward work, she has the weight and windage of her foremast.

Reaching she would be faster than a cutter, and there is no doubt headsails, loose footed and sheeted at the clew, lift rather than drive a vessel along. Dead before the wind she could not hold a cutter, as then she loses one-third of her sail area, her spinnaker boom setting on the foremast, while the sails between the two masts hang lifeless. I'm very fond of the schooner rig for three reasons: both masts are stayed together, so strong and reliable, the main topmast or fisherman's staysail set aloft catches the light airs there, and under foresail alone a schooner will heave to when the wind is strong enough for her to put her head under her wing.

My reason for holding up ocean racers as examples for cruisers is that being first and foremost a cruising man I have done just enough racing to understand that the ideal ocean racer is the ideal cruiser. Yachtsmen are generally divided into two groups, purely racing and purely cruising men, neither being able to see the merits of the other vessel. These ocean racers are cruisers as developed by racing men. Combining, as they do, the knowledge of cruising and racing men, they are interesting and instructive, and besides this,

they have to face every sort of weather in their races across wide oceans.

Ocean racers have done a great deal of research work for cruisers, they have proved the ability of the tall Bermudian mast to stand. Indeed, if we take the facts of races it would be considered stronger than the ordinary main and topmast rig, for records show that while many topmasts have carried away the Bermudian rig has stood.

The cutter rig is the fastest yet evolved, but for cruising, where ease in handling sails is of more importance than speed, the canvas should be split into smaller and more easily managed sails. This generally means a two- or three-masted rig. (Sometimes as many as seven masts being used.)

Niña's staysail schooner rig, offering, as it does, almost the speed of the cutter with the ease in handling of a schooner, is very tempting.

Uffa resented the short ends of *Niña*'s hull. One of his great precepts was drawing the lines out to their logical conclusion. His experiments with the relative size of mainsail to headsail, and the conclusions he drew from them, are interesting Later in yachting history the huge genoas made the mainsail no longer the *main* sail, and even going to windward the boats were sailed on the genoa.

The conception of *Niña*'s rig as a cutter with a large fore-triangle seems a little fanciful? However, while pursuing his argument on the usefulness of mainsail and fore-triangle while beating and running perhaps it was justified?

Leaving the accommodation open all the way through was a bold experiment in those days and apparently the owner had second thoughts about it later.

Lexia

Owner, Lt.-Col. T. P. Rose-Richards
Designer, Frederick Shepherd

LOA 60 ft. 0 in.
LWL 50 ft. 0 in.
Beam 13 ft. 6 in.
Draught 9 ft. 0 in.
Displacement 41 tons
Sail area 2,000 sq. ft.

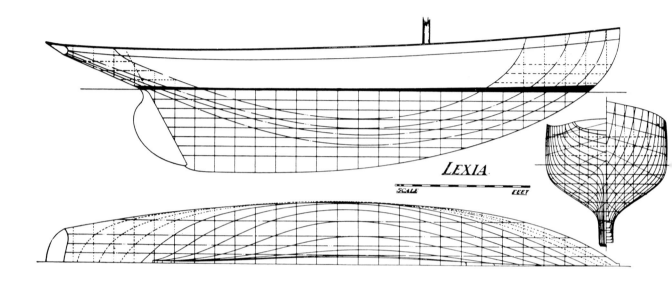

Lexia's owner, being unable to buy a second-hand cruiser to suit him, asked Shepherd to design him a ship in December 1930. In January the design was complete; work was commenced on her at the Lymington shipyard, and July saw her under way. The next month, August, she entered the Fastnet Race, and although not built to the Ocean Racing Club's formula, she managed to be the first British yacht on time allowance, *Dorade*, from America, winning the race.

In February 1932 she sailed from her home port, Chichester, to Madeira in 11 days 8 hours, in spite of the fact that she was hove to for sixty hours.

She started with a fine easterly wind down channel, which after three days developed into a gale in the Bay, and although still running comfortably *Lexia* was hove to with her mainsail rolled down to within three mast-hoops of the gaff jaws and lay quiet for two nights and days. Then the lacing along the gaff gave way, and *Lexia* was run off before the gale till this was renewed, when she was brought once more into the wind; but she shipped a green sea, which, breaking into the mainsail, practically submerged her, although the only damage was a sprung boom, which was seized with wire and gave no trouble.

Because the lacing of the gaff chafed through, *Lexia* has since used stops, a separate one at each eyelet, so that even if one does break the rest hold, whereas, if one part of a lacing chafes, the whole of the sail lacing on the gaff is adrift. Chafe is a great danger on long passages in fore-and-aft vessels, as generally a long distance is sailed with a fair wind, when the mainsail is eased on to the shrouds, whereas a square-rigged vessel has her sails forward of the mast and shrouds and so free from chafe.

Then again, take the different shrouds and stays set up by lanyards; the smaller the lanyard, the more parts it has and the neater it looks, and when new a small lanyard is as strong as a large one; but because it has three times the number of parts, it has more chance of chafe and each part is more easily chafed through, so it is not so good for its job.

A reef lacing has the advantage that it adjusts itself to the strain, and so pulls evenly all along the row of reef eyelets, and is thus less liable to tear the sail. Reef points all tied separately are unable to adjust themselves, and so often tear the sail at a point which, through being tied too tightly, takes more than its fair strain. But the reef lacing has the disadvantage of letting go every-

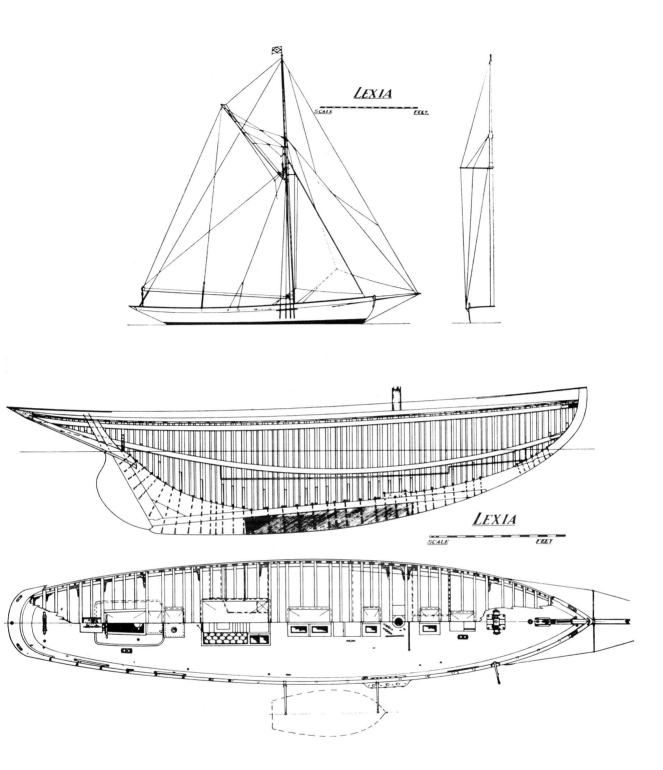

LEXIA

SCALE   FEET

LEXIA

SCALE   FEET

where once one part chafes through, although this again is an advantage in shaking out a reef in a hurry, when a slash with a knife at once frees all eyelets, and the tack and clew earings being released, the sail is ready for hoisting in a much shorter time than if it had had reef points. It follows that for racing lacings are best, and for cruising, reef points. *Lexia*, however, had neither, as her Woodnutt reefing gear enabled her to reef with her boom broad off, and the sail full of wind. This is how a roller sail should be reefed, as then the wind smooths out all wrinkles and a clean reef is taken in. A roller reefing boom should be larger on its outer

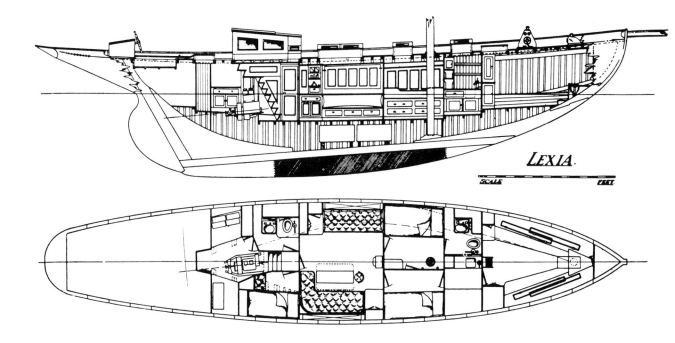

LEXIA.

SCALE   FEET

end, so that more sail is rolled up at this point, thus keeping the boom out of water. The topping lift takes the weight of the boom whilst reefing.

Lexia's original boom was 8 in. diameter, but because it was sprung, she had a new 9 in. boom made in City Island when she reached America. I think a boom 8 in. at the inner end and 9½ in. at the outer end would have been ideal.

From Madeira she sailed to Las Palmas and to Trinidad, taking 23 days on this last passage of 3,000 miles with a trysail and trysail topsail set on one hand, and a masthead spinnaker on the other, a comfortable and easy rig. From Trinidad, she visited Grenada, St. Lucia, St. Kitts, St. Thomas and the Virgin Group, and then on to Nassau, Miami, Charlestone and Norfolk. As she was earlier in America than anticipated, *Lexia* visited Boston before refitting in Long Island Sound for the Bermuda Race. This race was a reach and *Lexia* finished ninth against a fleet of 28 starters, taking 79 hours from Long Island Sound to Bermuda.

A day or so later she sailed for home, making the Lizard 20½ days out from Bermuda, and after a night in the Channel picked up her moorings in Chichester Harbour, which she had left six months previously.

It may surprise some readers to find a gaff cutter this size being built as late as 1931 — and entered in the Fastnet, and the Bermuda, too. However, she was not disgraced in either race and seems to have accomplished some useful cruising in her first year as well.

The description of *Lexia*'s troubles with her gaff rig is typical — though I would hasten to add that bermudian-rigged yachts had plenty of troubles when on long voyages. Few coastal sailors, accustomed to be at sea for a few days at a time, have any conception of the amount of chafe on a 3,000-mile down-wind Atlantic crossing in the Trades.

I dare say *Lexia* was a stirring sight when under full sail. I seem to have a hazy idea that her owner was "Tim" Rose-Richards, also well-known in motor-racing circles; but I may be wrong in that. (If I am right, it makes his choice of gaff rig the more surprising.)

Brilliant

Owner and Skipper, Walter Barnum
Designer, Olin Stephens

LOA 61 ft. 6 in.
LWL 49 ft. 0 in.
Beam 14 ft. 8 in.
Draught 8 ft 10 in.
Displacement 38¼ tons
Sail area 2,082 sq. ft.

For hard cruising off soundings Walter Barnum wanted a vessel, not only strongly rigged and masted, but also sturdily built, and *Brilliant* is, as a result of these requirements, a boat that can be driven hard without fear of anything falling down from aloft, or a sea straining her deck.

Yet in spite of this she is fast when conditions are right for her, as her passage across to England in June 1933 shows. Most people when they look at heavily built and powerfully lined vessels think that their best speed is in a gale of wind. Under such conditions they appear fast because of the spray flying, but practically every vessel makes its best speed with winds from 25 to 35 miles an hour; above that weight of wind reefing becomes necessary on account of the sea, and if a sailing vessel has not reached her maximum speed when it is blowing 30 miles an hour she is under canvassed.

And although *Brilliant*, to American ideas, seems to have little sail area, to our ideas this is not so, the difference being between the weather and leeside of the

Atlantic. American vessels generally have more sail than the English, due to the fact that our winds are generally stronger than those of America in summer. In the faintest of airs heavy vessels will sail and ghost along at an astonishing rate, for at such low speeds their full lines do not hinder them at all. The finer lined vessels show up to advantage when the wind freshens, as their maximum speed is more easily reached.

Brilliant must have had weather to her liking across the Atlantic, for she made the ocean part, from Block Island to the Bishops, in half an hour under 16 days. And the whole from City Island to Plymouth in 17 days 18 hours.

Her best run for five days was made with a southerly wind abeam blowing 25 miles an hour, and in those five days she sailed 1,077 miles; if not the best ever done by a boat that length, it is the best recorded. Averaging over 200 miles a day for five days is seldom the lot of small ocean-going yachts, for conditions must be right, as if the wind increases so that heavy seas make up steeply then the vessel has to be slowed or hove to, or if the wind falls away she slows up for want of it. The wind has to blow consistently between 20 and 40 miles an hour.

Dorade's best five-day run in the Transatlantic Race of 1931 was 1,013 miles, another average of over 200 a day, which shows that a fine-bottomed craft has a higher speed, or rather more easily reaches her highest speed, for *Dorade* is only three-quarter the length of *Brilliant* on the water-line, and as both were designed on the same drawing board it can be assumed that the lines are of equal merit, the difference being that one set is finer than the other.

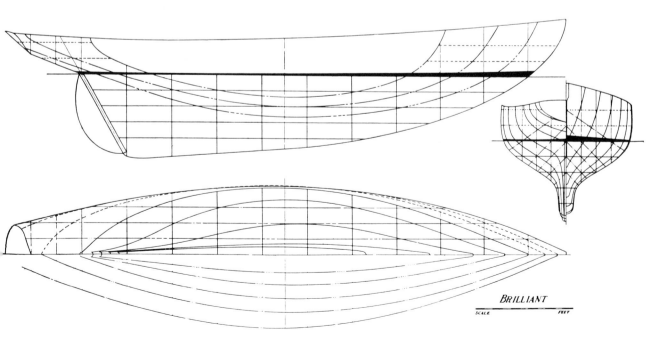

BRILLIANT
SCALE   FEET

Original caption: Brilliant. *The Fastnet Race was held in June, so the winds were light.*

Brilliant had sailed across for the Fastnet, but this race was in June and the weather therefore light, when her heavy rig was against her, as was *Lexia*'s. Neither of these did well.

On September 3 she sailed for home via Madeira and the North East Trades, and getting winds to her liking reached Madeira in 8 days, averaging 185 miles a day. As, in light weather, we had taken 14 days over this same course in *Diablesse*, the news of this startled me, for I was in America and on Long Island at the time; and bursting into Olin's office at City Island I

breathlessly (having run miles) asked him for *Brilliant*'s plans for this book, as I was trying to collect the very best designs for it. And he said, "Yes."

From Madeira she took 3 days to Tenerife, and 23 days from there to Bermuda and another six from there to City Island, experiencing good weather all the time, only having to stow her foresail and topsail for six hours in the Gulf Stream, but at Montauk Point she picked up the weather she revelled in, and finished the passage in 10 hours, passing Montauk at 9.30 p.m. and picking up her moorings off City Island at 7.30 a.m.

Just 10 knots, a Brilliant end to *Brilliant*'s Brilliant cruise.

The lines are those of a fast yet very weatherly cruiser, with clean easy buttocks and powerful sections standing out from the rest. These two combined make a fast reaching vessel, the sections giving power to carry sail and the easy buttocks making for high speeds. Her best day's run, when she logged 230 miles, which averages 9.58 knots, was made with a beam wind and shows her ability reaching.

Brilliant has a chart room aft on the port side, a useful and unusual thing in such a small vessel, opposite which are oilskin lockers and a seat. The saloon is forward of this, then comes a single cabin to port, and the wash room to starboard, and the galley divides this from the fo'c'sle.

Her area of sail is normal, but divided into a snug and strong schooner rig, which makes her look very seaworthy and workmanlike. Such a rig makes one wish to cruise round the world in *Brilliant*, for any one of her spars could be replaced, in almost any part of the world, although it is very unlikely that any would carry away.

I would have thought that, even to American eyes, the sail area would have seemed adequate. A squaresail is shown by dotted lines on the foremast, though it is not mentioned in the text. A squaresail is awkward to rig and handle on a small fore-and-aft rigged vessel, so perhaps it was omitted?

When ocean cruising, as opposed to racing, 100 miles a day is usually enough to keep every one happy, even today, so 200 a day is certainly "going". *Brilliant* made 230 on one day, an average of 9.58 knots; but she was 49 ft. on the water-line, which is a fair sized vessel.

The concluding sentence has a wistful ring now. Commercial sail still lingered on over large areas of the globe in those days and the timber built yachts could get some sort of repair done, even if the finish was not quite up to yacht standard. No doubt the makers of alloy masts and spars will retort that, with the service they offer, replacements can be flown anywhere in a matter of days. So they can—at a price!

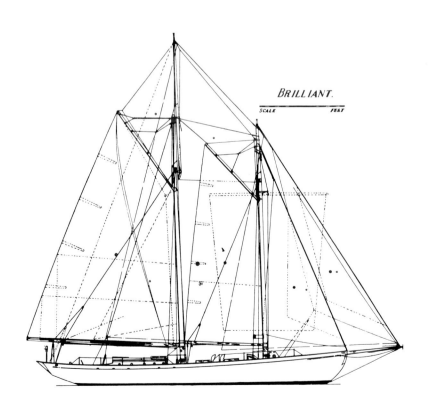

BRILLIANT.

SCALE   FEET

Dorade

Owner and Skipper, Olin Stephens
Designer, Olin Stephens

LOA 52 ft. 0 in.
LWL 37 ft. 3 in.
Beam 10 ft. 3 in.
Draught 8 ft. 0 in.
Displacement 14¾ tons
Sail area 1,100 sq. ft.

At least Olin was skipper till 1932 when, having to race his 6-metre *Nancy* in England, he handed *Dorade* over to his brother "Rod", who with her won the Bermuda

Race for her class that year. This year he sailed her from America to Norway, down to Cowes, England, and back to America after winning the Fastnet Race.

The first time I met *Dorade* was just two days before the start of the Transatlantic Race, 1931, at Newport, Rhode Island. That night we all attended the dinner given by the Cruising Club of America, and there George Roosevelt, in yarning to me, said that he did not think the club should allow such fragile boats as *Dorade* to race across the Atlantic. As this was only my third visit to America it seemed wrong to disagree with a name like Roosevelt, especially when its owner had a big black mistress, so I said yes and no at what I judged to be the right moments. Three weeks later, when we all arrived in England, we found this fragile vessel

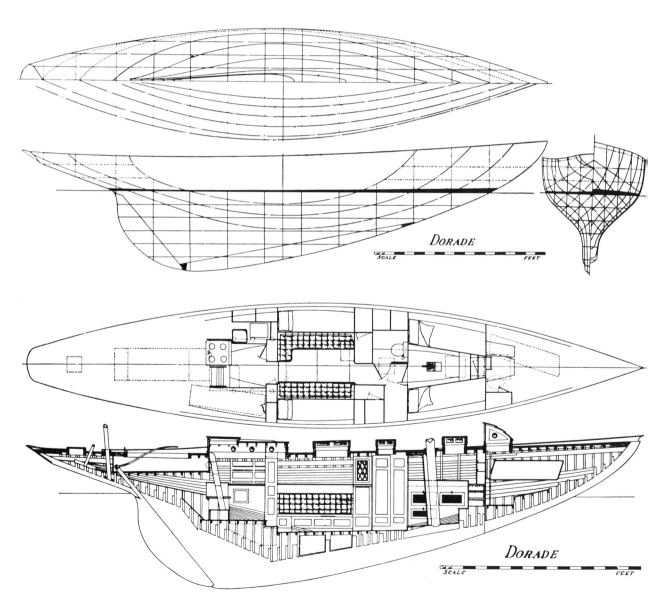

DORADE

SCALE   FEET

DORADE

SCALE   FEET

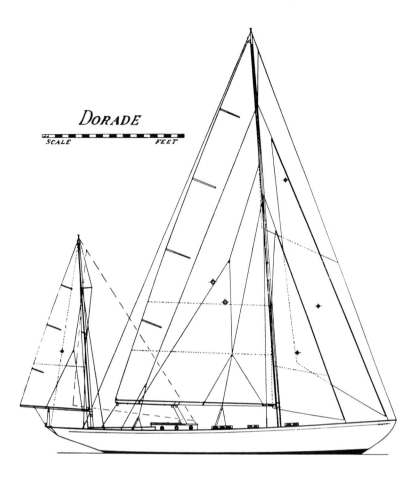

there to meet us. *Dorade* had beaten all her larger rivals, including *Mistress*, by days, so had won the Transatlantic race without calling upon her time allowance. After this she won the Fastnet Race (1931) almost as nicely, and the sympathy towards the smaller boats began to turn to understanding, and when she sailed across the Atlantic to win the Fastnet again last year (1933) she convinced committees that smaller boats, well sailed, are far faster than their handicap supposes. In the light of this understanding it is probable that handicaps will be readjusted.

In looking at the lines of *Dorade* it is well to pause a moment to think of her remarkable record, almost a possible (as we'd say on a rifle range). 1930 second in the Bermuda Race for her class, 1931 won the Transatlantic Race and the Fastnet Race, 1932 won the Bermuda Race for her class, 1933 sailed across the Atlantic, won the Fastnet Race and then sailed back to America. Her greatest achievement, however, is her return voyage to America this summer: Cowes, England, to Larchmont, America, in 26 days 15 hours. (This remarkable passage to windward across the

Ocean is dealt with in chapters on the North Atlantic.) Off the wind *Dorade* is as fast as a 10-metre, and to windward half a minute a mile slower, and reaching across the Sound this summer in a smart breeze the 12-metres had difficulty in dropping us astern. So *Dorade* is fast beyond all doubt, all possible doubt whatever.

Dorade's ends are not chopped off, the bow and stern being the natural ending of her lines, and these overhangs help in a seaway when they increase her effective length from 37 to 52 ft., thus increasing her natural speed and fore and aft stability. Her deep draught partially compensates for her narrow beam, and is an advantage to windward.

Dorade does not come to the ideal proportions for cruisers, as given in the chapter on that subject, and so is very instructive. Her narrow beam is balanced by her deep draught, her light displacement by a small sail area, and her narrow floor space forces her freeboard higher, for headroom.

. *Dorade* with her easy sections is at her best to windward and running, all her remarkable days' runs being made with the wind well aft. These records show the effect of the difference between the two sets of lines.

The yawl rig was chosen for handicap purposes; without her mizen *Dorade* would still rate the same, so as, under the rule, the mizen with its staysail is free, it is well worth having. Such a mizen is of little value dead before the wind, for besides spoiling the clean run of wind into the mainsail and spinnaker, it tends to drive the vessel into the wind; while to windward, because it is in the dirty wind off the mainsail, it has to be sheeted so tightly that it has little forward drive. However, reaching in light to strong winds, the mizen, with its staysail, is a great driver, and when the wind is really strong *Dorade*, with her mizen stowed, will steer far more easily than a cutter, for her boom is so short.

The double headsail rig makes for ease in handling in hard weather, for by hauling the staysail to weather *Dorade* will slow down, and her crew, waiting till her speed has dropped to 3 knots, quietly change jibs or do whatever the weather calls for. In light weather the two headsails are stowed and a large Yankee jib topsail set from the stem to the masthead, thus filling in the whole of the fore triangle. This sail was the only unhandy thing aboard *Dorade*, for in tacking we had to pass it between the jib and the jibtopsail stays, where there was only 18 in. of space on deck. About 1860 our square-rigged merchantmen changed from large single to double topsails, as they were so much easier to handle if split in two. *Dorade*'s double headsails do for her what the double topsails did for the square-rigged merchantmen. Not only is it easier to set two, sheet two, or change two smaller sails, but a boat is often able by simply stowing one small sail, to carry on through a squall and re-set it immediately afterwards. The ease with which *Dorade* is handled was impressed upon me last summer, when standing ashore at Oyster Bay, I saw Rod sail her in single handed, pick up his mooring, stow sails and jump into the International 14-footer *Arrow*, which his confederate, Porter Buck, had meanwhile sailed out alongside, all within 8 minutes. And to crown this, the *Arrow* won.

Although merchantmen the world over adopted the double topsail our Men-of-War did not as, having ample man power, they did not have to study ease in handling sails.

Dorade rolled when running, but this was largely cured last summer, before she left Cowes for America, when a balance reef was put in, running from the tack to 3 ft. above the clew; this must have kept her mainsail from going forward of the mast aloft when the main sheet was eased, for she rolled much less. It also prevented the boom from tripping in the sea when running, and Rod thinks this reef might even have been 4 ft. deep at the clew.

The mainsheet leading off the centre of the boom tends to prevent it lifting when the sheet is started. The fault of the modernised Bermudian rig lies in the fact that when the sheet is started, instead of the boom squaring off as it does in the gaff rig, the sail aloft falls

away, and it is usual to see this tall rig with the mainsail squared off on to the crosstrees, while the main boom is still at 45 degrees.

Her mast is well rigged fore and aft, forward there are three stays, jibtopsail, jib and staysail, and there are three backstays each straining aft from the points on the mast where the corresponding stay pulls forward. The drift of the backstays aft is good, that taking the pull of the staysail being the same distance abaft the mast as the forestay is forward. The jib and jibtopsail backstays have even more drift aft than the base of the foretriangle, and so it is that *Dorade*'s mast stands perfectly straight no matter how hard she is pressed. This in turn gives headsails with luffs that stand and a nicely-setting mainsail.

Wire halyards and winches did away with the necessity for setting the halyards up every watch, and winches taking the load off the sheets enable one man to trim sheets down instead of three; she had twelve winches all told. The same cruising yachtsman who scorns the winches on an Ocean Racer admires and praises the handiness of a Thames barge, losing sight of the fact that it is only the winches aboard that enable two men to handle these 100-ton vessels.

The fo'c'sle with its single cot is used as a sail room, as *Dorade* has always carried an all-amateur crew; abaft this is the fore-cabin with two berths, which are faced with plaited gratings for ventilation. A wash room to port and a locker and bookcase to starboard divide this cabin from the saloon, which has two sleeping berths with settees in front. The saloon table at one time had its legs upon the floor, which with *Dorade*'s narrow floor-space (2 ft. 8 in.), gave little leg-room for the crew. This year the table legs were inverted and made fast to the deckbeams, turning the tables upon the swing table, for it altered it from an unstable table into a stable table, the legs down from the deck forming perfect life rails.

Abaft the saloon to port is the galley, in its right and proper place on a small boat, for here it is near the centre of the see-saw, where the motion is least. Opposite the galley is the chart table with its electric log and compass enabling the navigator to tell exactly the course and speed without enquiring of the man at the helm. This log is also easily read from the tiller, and it gave my vanity a nasty shock, for, before steering *Dorade* with her tell-tale log, I fondly imagined that I took a boat quite nicely to windward. The art of steering to windward lies in holding the boat high yet footing fast; *Dorade*'s best was four points off the wind and just over 6 knots. And sitting steering her, I saw that log dropping down as low as $5\frac{3}{4}$ knots without my feeling that I was starving her of wind, or the compass showing that I had pinched her above her best course.

That fine point where the last ounce is coaxed out of a boat to windward is very difficult to define. Hence it is, no doubt, that boats go some days better than others: the helmsman is able, without effort, to hit off this point exactly and sail a wonderful race. On other days, instead of winning he comes in well down the list, quite convinced that something is wrong with his boat. How often we hear the expression "My boat would not go to day," when it should be "I could not get my boat to go to-day." Yacht owners, who claim the credit when they win and blame their boats when they lose, remind me of my young days, for when I was naughty my father would say to mother, "That nipper of your's ——," but when I won medals he'd say, "My son, etc., etc."

Dorade's small tiller shows that she is easy on her helm, and proves her to be a well-balanced boat. The tiny lever seen half-way down the tiller locks and unlocks it in an instant, and the duckboard stretched across the cockpit makes steering an easy job. The tiller has a rather surprised expression as it peeps out from under the deck upon the world. This is caused by the mizen mast, which forces the rudder post to be cut off short, as can be seen from the plan.

This year *Dorade*'s ventilators were improved, for where they originally led directly below, they now lead into a box on deck, from which the air is taken below by another pipe standing several inches above the deck. When a wave is taken down the ventilator it partly fills the box and escapes through tiny scuppers, without rising above the level of the pipe leading below. Therefore water cannot find its way below unless two seas are shipped down the ventilator in rapid succession, and this, so far, has not occurred.

The beams run right across under the skylight, making the deck very strong and easy to keep watertight. Farther aft, however, the deck beams cannot run clear across, as the coach roof is built here to give headroom in the galley and protect the helmsman in the cockpit.

In this description of *Dorade* I have tried to make it clear that her ability and success does not lie so much in any special point, but in the perfection of every detail. The comfort of the helmsman, his being able to read on the log directly he starves her on the wind, the position of the galley, the ease with which the navigator can work, the staying of the mast all help to make *Dorade* such an able little ship. And she has always had a crew to match this perfection.

Dorade was legendary in her day. The Stephens brothers, Olin and Rod, were still youthful and this cast a glamour over their achievements. I was very young myself and I remember thinking: "That little boat crossed the Atlantic in just over a fortnight—and a liner takes five days". I was very impressed. We thought of her as a "little" boat and I am surprised to find now that she was 52 ft. over all.

Dorade put Olin Stephens on the map as a designer. On this side of the Atlantic we only thought of one firm in connection with yacht design in America—Sparkman & Stephens. (The feeling was not quite so wide-spread in their own country, as I subsequently discovered.)

Thus early, Rod Stephens was already beginning to assume the role he has since occupied of a "test-pilot" trying out his brother's drawing-board and towing-tank ideas at sea. It has proved to be a wonderfully productive combination. Those two, between them, must know all there is to know about yachts and their gear.

Dorade should not be thought a forerunner of the beamy centre-board yawls which later dominated the American offshore scene. Her hull shape was quite different—being much nearer earlier "metre" boats.

She gave her name to a water trap ventilator, variations of which are used today. On the rig there were two sets of runners. She was probably as near perfection as could be attained in those days and she pointed the way ahead towards a new breed of ocean racer.

Dorade is now based at Seattle, where she is maintained as a cruiser in excellent condition.

Rosemary

Owner and Skipper, Isaac Bell
Designer, William Fife

LOA 52 ft. 0 in.
LWL 36 ft. 0 in.
Beam 12 ft. 0 in.
Draught 7 ft. 0 in.
Displacement 17 tons
Sail area 1,400 sq. ft.

The race round the Isle of Wight on June 17, 1933, held by the Island Sailing Club, showed me that *Rosemary* was beyond all doubt a fast and seaworthy vessel, for she won this race under her trysail after her mainsail had been blown away.

The start was at 8.00 a.m., with the wind WNW, strong enough to cause quite a sea, as it was against the ebb tide; and the fleet started under shortened sail for the beat to the Needles.

As helmsman of *Daedalus*, a sixty-year-old cutter, of the Itchen Ferry type, sturdy, but slow to windward in a lop, I gazed with envy and admiration at *Rosemary* sailing a point higher in the wind and travelling three miles to our two, as she sailed out from under our lee and was soon hull down ahead, never expecting for a moment to see her again till we had finished our fifty-four miles race, and were safely back at Cowes.

We had a full mainsail, staysail and jib, and although no topsail, had all the sail we could carry, but in spite of this *Daedalus* seemed slow, for every time her bow rose to a sea her stern dropped and dragged dead water. She would have travelled faster through the water under the North Shore where the tide was less and so the sea calmer, but not so fast over the ground, so we kept her to the Island side of the Solent, where the tides run stronger and seas steeper.

Out in the Channel the flood tide runs to the east and the ebb to the west, and so it is in the Solent, but through Spithead, between Bembridge and Cowes, there is a different stream, for the last part of the ebb and the first half of the flood run eastward, while the last of the flood and the first of the ebb run to the westward.

As everywhere else in the world, the tide is weaker along the shore; most bays, if deep, have eddy tides running directly opposite to the main tide, and for this reason the tide turns an hour or two earlier in these bays and near the shore. Because the tides are so strong and regular, a yacht sailing round the Isle of Wight has no need of an engine, for if worked properly these tides will take her where she would go without any fuss or effort. For instance, a small yacht could drop out of Yarmouth Harbour on the last of the ebb, which, taking her out past the pier would put her into the young flood, and this taking her to Cowes at 3 knots would save any engine work at all in a calm.

Rosemary too worked this strong tide, but her overhangs were of the greatest help to her in the sea, holding her steady fore and aft, for as soon as she tried to drop her bow and stern her sailing length increased and prevented her doing so.

And so we fought our way down to the Needles, where there was such a steep sea running over the Bridge and through the Needles Channel that in *Daedalus* we eased our main sheet right off, and sailed her at about 3 knots with only the headsails drawing, as charging into the steep seas she seemed intent on bursting both headsails, for she dipped them into solid water. *Mermaid*, a much larger vessel than *Daedalus*, alongside and to windward, did not ease anything; she buried her jib in a sea heavier than most, and away went both jib and bowsprit. So she had a fine mess to clear up forward. For the bowsprit, held by the wire shrouds and bobstay, tried hard to punch holes in her bow, and it was with great difficulty and a certain amount of danger of being swept overboard, that *Mermaid*'s crew at last tidied up the broken gear as she ran back into the Solent.

The *Enid*, some ten minutes astern, plunging into the steep breakers off the Needles Channel, burst open her garboards, and was at once filled above her floorboards. She turned back and ran into Alum Bay, whilst her crew bailed hard with buckets in order to keep her afloat. They just managed to get into the bay before she foundered in 15 ft., where she lay with her spars showing above the water until the seas battered her to pieces.

This was at 10.00 a.m. In *Daedalus* we rounded the Bridge Buoy and squared away for St. Catherine's, only to find that the strong ebb on our bow pushed us seawards, so we had to gybe to get into the easier tide of Brook Bay; all the crew were against this manoeuvre because of the sea, but we were racing, and as I had the tiller there was little hesitation or argument, for they were too busy with backstays to talk, and we were soon in the slack water under the land and gaining rapidly on everyone, even *Rosemary*, for we were the only boat to gybe and take advantage of the slacker water. Off shore the strong ebb would run for at least another two hours, so whilst we in *Daedalus* were foaming along at 7 knots with a fair tide of 1 knot, thus travelling 8 knots over the ground, *Rosemary* was doing 9 knots against a 3 knot tide, and thus only 6 knots over the ground. In addition to this we had the wind and tide together, and so could carry a spinnaker, though when it was set I had to call for help on the tiller.

So we came to St. Catherine's, *Daedalus* being second to round with only *Rosemary* in front. We were well within our time allowance, and would have felt very sprightly had the wind shown any sign of shifting SW, and so altering the beat from Bembridge Ledge to Cowes into a reach, for with that long beat against the tide we knew that *Rosemary* would lose us again. On the run across to St. Catherine's, *Guenora*, who not only

ROSEMARY.

SCALE   FEET.

had her topsail stowed but also two reefs in her mainsail, showed how easily a boat could run if not driven, for although a much faster vessel, she was not only travelling at our speed and sailing along as quietly as a lamb, whilst we in *Daedalus* had two men on the tiller all the time our spinnaker was set.

On the reach across Sandown Bay *Rosemary* and *Otter* sailed away from us, and we rounded Bembridge Ledge third, with that dreaded beat in front of us, during which we knew *Daedalus* could not do well against the boats with overhangs, which would aid them in a seaway.

By the time we were beating through the Forts *Rosemary* was off Ryde Pier, and down came the strongest squall of the day; it split *Rosemary*'s mainsail right across from luff to leach, blew in half *Guenora*'s jib just to leeward of us, but did not affect *Daedalus* except to stun her, for instead of going faster in the increased

wind she slowed. This was probably due to the fact that watching the water to windward, we had seen this squall bearing down on us, and were ready, so when it struck us I sailed *Daedalus* along as fine as possible, starving the sails of wind as much as I could without letting them shake, for one shake and a sail would have split in that wind, just as it would have done if given the full weight of it.

Slowly we tacked very short boards all along the sands, and weathering Ryde Pier were able to ease the tide, and making better progress finished fifth to *Rosemary*, *Felise*, *Otter*, and *Guenora*.

We had the satisfaction of knowing that in such strong weather the four ahead were all much faster vessels, as were many astern of *Daedalus*.

Rosemary had won a wonderful race, and the fact that she was able not only to hold but to increase her lead under her storm trysail, which she had set after her mainsail had split off Ryde Pier, shows the strength of the wind and also the ability of *Rosemary*.

When I was yacht-broking my old boss always reckoned a Fife boat to be worth about half as much again as any other of the same age, so Uffa's rather extravagant praise of *Rosemary* did not altogether surprise me. "Ikey" Bell was a redoubtable skipper, too.

The tidal streams around the Isle of Wight are a rare puzzle for the newcomer. He thinks of the ebb as flowing down Southampton Water and out around either end of the Island. Then he discovers that the stream inside the Island runs in conformity with the main Channel stream outside, so that when the ebb is running out through the Needles it is entering through Spithead. Having disposed of that difficulty, though, there yet remain all the little flaws and back-eddies around every minor bay or headland to be learned. The whole forms a very complex pattern and knowledge of where the tide will turn slightly earlier inshore can win or lose a race. It is surprising to find visiting foreign helmsmen during Cowes Week doing so well, for if ever local knowledge ought to count it is here.

Rosemary may be considered a "period piece", so representative is she of ideas current at the time; but the boom on the foot of the foresail is unusual for a British boat, and as shown on the sail plan drawing appears to have a slight curvature in it.

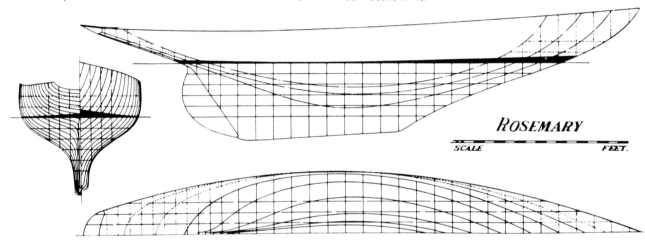

ROSEMARY

SCALE   FEET.

Twilight

LOA 28 ft. 0 in.
LWL 27 ft. 6 in.
Beam 9 ft. 0 in.
Draught 5 ft. 10 in.
Displacement 7 tons
Sail area 670 sq. ft.

Falmouth Quay Punts are without doubt weatherly vessels, for, as they were designed as handmaidens to the sailing ships calling at Falmouth for orders, they had to brave the wind and sea, summer and winter, between the ship and the quay, and when without a job they went seeking a ship away down channel.

Their mainmasts were cut off at the upper peak halyard block, to enable them to clear the yard arms of the ships they served. The lines and sail plan of *Twilight* illustrate the characteristics of this type of vessel.

So Spot and I, journeying to Norway to sail *Twilight* home to Cowes, had no fears as to her seaworthiness and ability to take what came in the way of weather, although some Norwegian friends, not used to this type of vessel, were doubtful of her ability.

On the way to Norway our steamer met a heavy gale from the north-east, which delayed her some hours, and as this gale was still blowing when we arrived in Kristiansand, we waited three days for it to ease down, for whereas at sea a small vessel manfully rides it out, it is wrong to start out in a gale, and Marine Insurance Companies of small vessels would, I think, be within their rights if they refused to pay insurance on a small vessel that, without just cause, put to sea in a full gale.

And so we waited, and on Thursday, April 29, 1926, put to sea at 5.00 p.m. with three reefs in the mainsail, a reef in the staysail, and our jib and mizen unrigged and stowed below in the fo'c'sle. The driving sails are those in the centre, and not at the ends of a vessel, and even with this small amount of sail *Twilight* had all she could carry, for there was still plenty of weight in the wind, and a high sea running from four days of a hard gale that was only just starting to ease.

In the first 24 hours we travelled 125 miles, and considering the sea running and the overall length of

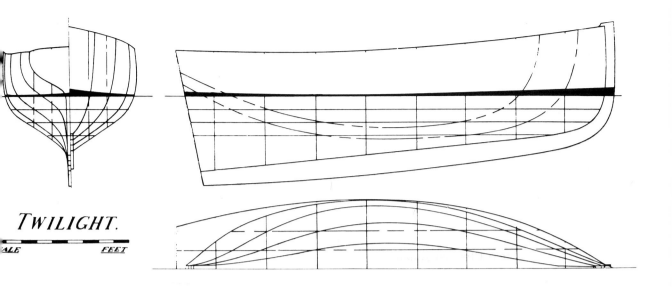

TWILIGHT.

our vessel, this pleased us. Day followed day, and still it blew hard and cold from the north-east, and coming down to the Dutch coast we headed in for the *Terschelling Light Ship* on Saturday afternoon to check our position. The sunset looked wicked, and fearing an on-shore gale from the north-west, I let her go on out to sea again without sighting the *Terschelling*, so that, when the gale arrived, we should be able to drive away before it for days if necessary without fear of that lee shore.

We drove and drove her out towards the centre of the North Sea. Besides the three reefs in the mainsail the gaff jaws had been lowered on to the main boom, so that we only showed a small triangle of mainsail and the staysail. Even with this small amount of sail we were travelling so fast that *Twilight* trembled throughout as she rushed down the face of the seas.

At 3.00 a.m. Spot yelled for help, as he could not hold her on her course, and jumping out of my bunk to his assistance, I was just in time to see a huge sea

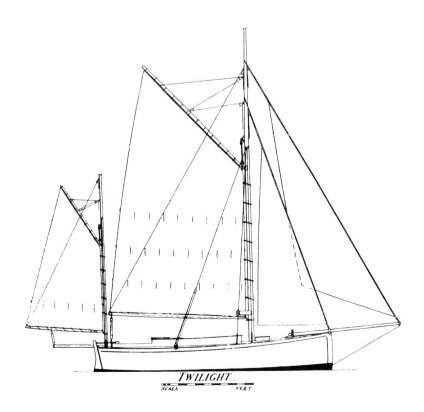

TWILIGHT.

SCALE   FEET

39

curling in over the stern the height of our mizen mast. We were pooped, and very heavily; I was knocked backwards into the cabin but not hurt, and was soon on deck stowing the rest of the mainsail, after which *Twilight* with only her staysail set was easier to steer.

Turning in again I left Spot at the helm, still fighting to clear the Dutch coast. Later that night, with only the staysail on her, she started pulling seas aboard again over her transom, so we streamed the drogue out aft, and, lashing the tiller, let her drive very slowly before the gale, which was fortunately due north, so that we could by now drive the full length of the North Sea from the north of Holland to France without fear of land.

We took turns watching for ships that might run us down till daylight, when we both turned in for the day. That heavy sea we had taken aboard had, in spite of her self-bailing cockpit, filled her above the level of the bunks, but we slept in wet clothes and bedding without harm, although it was bitterly cold. After laying to our drogue for 24 hours, during which time no really heavy water came aboard, we were able to haul it in and drove on under staysail only for some hours, when the wind easing still more allowed us to show the peak of our mainsail.

It was cheering to see the Foreland, as it seemed that now we should storm along to the Wight in smooth water under the lee of the land. Just before the noon sight the wind had eased enough to allow us to carry full mainsail, and soon after the spinnaker was set, but this was only for an hour, for a squall out of a clear sky hit us, bursting the spinnaker and springing the boom.

The remains were sadly gathered in, and the wind continuing to freshen forced me to take in one reef after another until all three were in again, and we could do no more but lower the gaff jaws on the boom again.

Twilight, designed and built in 1904 by W. E. Thomas of Falmouth, is a fine example of a Quay Punt, and is a credit to her designer and builder, for she withstood the gales of the North Sea manfully and inspired us with confidence throughout our stormy passage.

At one time I had an all-consuming ambition to own a Falmouth Quay Punt. I wanted to go ocean cruising, I realized that my finances would never permit my owning other than a very small boat, and this was my ideal. I believed that only the work-boat type was fit to go offshore, and that yachts were butterflies which could only perform in the Solent on a summer's afternoon. (When I ultimately sailed across the Atlantic, about twenty years afterwards, it was in a light displacement ocean racer!)

Considering she was the antithesis of all his pet theories, I think Uffa deals very fairly with *Twilight*'s performance on the passage from Norway. Interesting are his remarks about the drogue. All the early books on cruising which I read were obsessed with this theory about "... holding her head up to it ..." with a sea-anchor in a gale.

Vigilant

Designer, Owner and Skipper, Uffa Fox

LOA 34 ft. 6 in.
LWL 25 ft. 6 in.
Beam 6 ft. 4 in.
Draught 4 ft. 3 in.
Displacement 2 tons
Sail area 236 sq. ft.

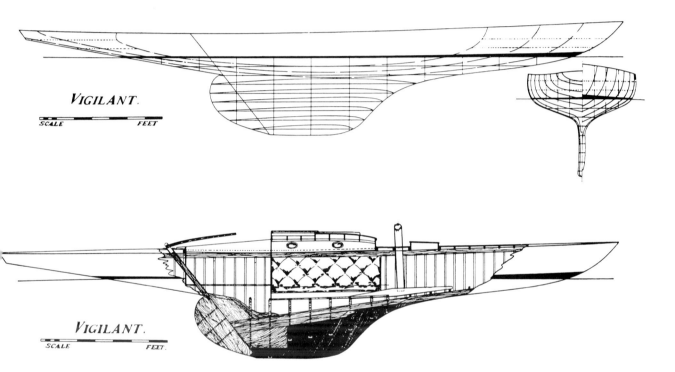

Practically every small sailing vessel with outside ballast and a deck is able to stand far more hard driving than her crew of human beings, and this fact, among others, accounts for so many different types being held up as ideal for cruising, where gales have to be weathered at sea. If man were able to stand more than small ships, in the way of hard weather, we should soon arrive at the ideal sailing vessel, and cruisers would all be alike just as the international racing class boats are.

The cruise described in the following pages was made by a boat of the type that is generally looked upon as being quite unsuited to the open sea. She is Bermudian rigged, with a mast longer than her hull, the halyards and luff rope of the mainsail run up inside this hollow spar, while her displacement to length is so light that the "Q" class, which races on the Solent, refuses to let her compete. Compared to the inter-

national 6-metre yacht, she is of about the same size, with half the sail area and half the displacement. Without holding this extreme type of racing boat up as ideal for deep water work, I should like to point out that *Vigilant* made her cruise to Sweden and back to Cowes in a summer noted for its strong winds, and five different times encountered wind of gale force—registered ashore, not by her crew.

While chasing away before three of these gales, she seemed to tear along at twice her natural speed, which suggests that her press of sail was three times as much as she should carry.

Vigilant did not suffer at all through this harsh treatment, except that the paint came off her seams under water near her entrance, which would have happened to any new vessel, and is the reason for not coppering a new ship until she is a year or so old, and

Vigilant, *22-square metre, with Uffa at the helm.*

settled down in life.

Vigilant was launched, had two spins to air her new sails, and was then loaded up with food, spare sails and other gear for her cruise to Sweden, leaving Cowes at 6.30 p.m. on Monday, June 30.

We were a crew of three. Dr. R. T. Cooke, who is the owner of the 5-tonner *Enid*, and is grandson of the famous E. W. Cooke, R.A., Bob Dickerson, one of my old sea scouts now grown up to a man-sized engineer, and myself, owner.

The weather report looked as though we were in for a dead beat in a jump, as it stated "wind 30 miles an hour SE", but as we beat through the Spithead forts, heavy rain squalls from all directions, with violent thunder and lightning, knocked the wind down to faint airs from all points of the compass. With hardly a breath of wind we sailed up Channel past the *Owers, Royal Sovereign* and *South Goodwin Light Vessel*, taking three days to do what we could have done in one with a decent breeze, and at 9.45 p.m. July 2, with the *North Goodwin Light Vessel* close abeam, we set our course for the *Terschelling Light Vessel*, 180 miles away NE ¾ E.

On July 3, at 6.00 p.m. Latitude 52.06, Longitude 2.50 E, we were passed by the *Bremen* close to leeward, which showed we were right on our course.

We have not space for Uffa's description of his cruise in *Vigilant*. The passage from Cowes to Sandhamn, in Sweden, was accomplished in 17 days and a variety of weather conditions accompanied it. There were squalls and a period of thick fog in the North Sea before they made the Elbe and entered the Kiel Canal. It was hard going part of the way up the Eastern Swedish seaboard, too. They carried evening clothes, with stiff shirt-fronts, and it was as well they did because Uffa was presented with a cup, not for the racing at Sandhamn, where he made a very poor showing, but for the cruise out from England. The home-ward passage, Sandhamn to Lowestoft, took 14 days, including 150 miles dead to windward in 48 hours, with a heavy sea, averaging 3 knots. From Lowestoft they took her through onto Oulton Broad where there was International Fourteen Foot dinghy racing in which Uffa had an interest, and later back to Cowes.

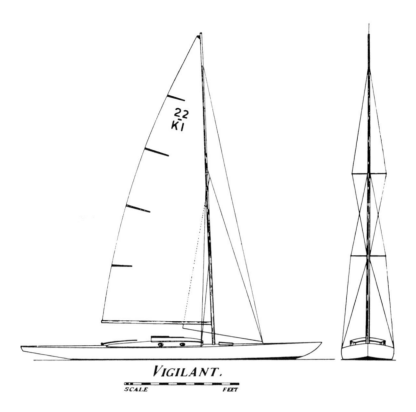

VIGILANT.

SCALE ▬▬▬▬ FEET

Crystal

Owner, David Anderson
Designer, Frederick Shepherd

LOA 30 ft. 6 in.
LWL 22 ft. 0 in.
Beam 8 ft. 6 in.
Draught 4 ft. 3 in.
Displacement 4·9 tons
Sail area 479 sq. ft.

Crystal is one of the best, if not the best cruiser of her size and type ever designed, for although only 22 ft. on the line she has 6 ft. of headroom for a length of 10 ft. with a 2 ft. 9 in. floor space, and this on a very pretty set of lines.

Generally such headroom in so small a vessel is only obtained through distorting her lines and proportions, so that she sacrifices her sailing qualities for her accommodation, but here accommodation, beauty of line and proportion are nicely blended.

The lines are powerful, and although firm, the bilge is not hard and harsh, and in looking at it it must be remembered that the smaller the boat the more powerful should be her sections generally.

Her accommodation is well thought out, and she can sleep four, one in the fo'c'sle, two in the saloon, where

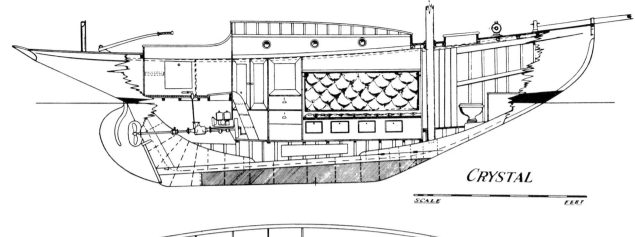

CRYSTAL

SCALE   FEET

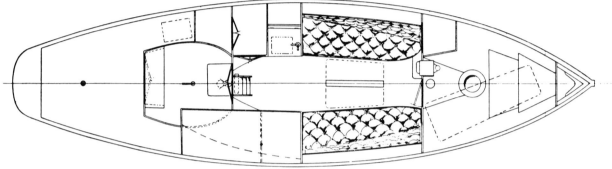

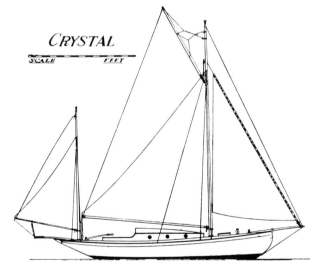

CRYSTAL

SCALE   FEET

the backs of the settees fold down and so make beds at night, while during the day they fold the bedding back out of sight, and the fourth in the berth abaft the saloon on the starboard side. This in time of peace is a sideboard.

Opposite this berth is the galley, well aft, as it should be in a small vessel, for here in the centre of the seesaw the motion is least, the cook can stand up, for there is 6 ft. headroom here, and also the smell and fumes from the cooking and stove are soon out of the sliding hatch.

The coach roof 2 ft 9 in. wide, as is the floor space, gives full headroom over the floor, and being so narrow does not interfere with the deck space at all, so that the 305 sq. ft. mainsail can easily be set or reefed or taken in.

There is no mention of a chart-table—a curious omission in many of these old designs. It would have been easy to contrive one folding down over the bunk opposite the galley. In the account of the voyage round the world in *Svaap* given in the book "Deep Water and Shoal", William A. Robinson is shown working at his charts on the ordinary cabin table. It could be a posed picture, or was this normal practice at that time?

The high-peaked mainsail on *Crystal* was, I think, more often seen in America than here. It was a means of achieving more area high up without the complication of a topsail. The forestay running to the bowsprit end was a source of weakness, since if anything happened to the bowsprit the mast was immediately in jeopardy. The foresail looks as though it is set on a wooden roller—providing reefing as well as furling. The trouble was the wire stay emerging from the bottom of the roller. It was subjected to severe kinking strains here, because the roller was rigid and the wire flexible.

Britannia

Designer, G. L. Watson
Owner, His Majesty King George V

LOA 122 ft. 0 in.
LWL 87 ft. 0 in.
Beam 23 ft. 3 in.
Draught 15 ft. 0 in.
Displacement 153½ tons
Sail area 10,797 (1893) and 9,235 (1933)

"*Britannia* the pride of the Ocean,
Beloved by the brave and the free.
The Shrine of a Sailor's devotion
What ship can compare unto thee?"

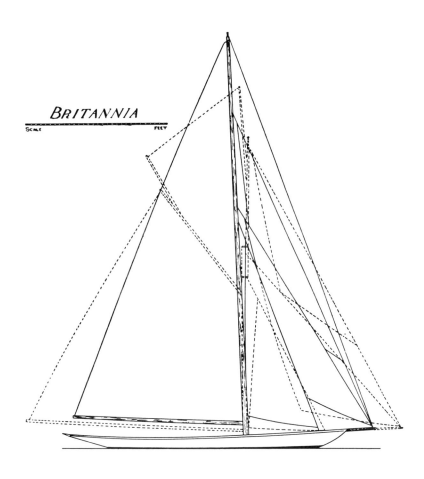

BRITANNIA

Britannia brings home many lessons. She proves that beauty is a matter of education, for when she first breasted the waters forty years ago she was considered ugly to a generation educated to admire the hollow clipper bow, while to-day she is held by all as a model of grace and beauty. "Handsome is that handsome does."

Her life-history is instructive to designers, builders,

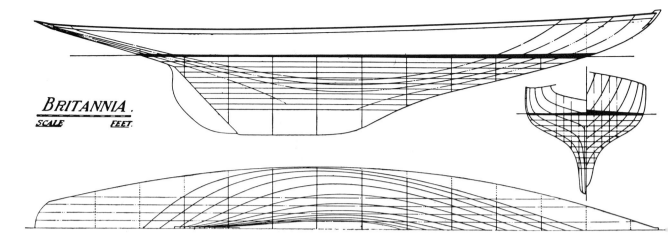

owners and rule makers. For she points out to these, that what is good for one is good for all, as each depends upon the other. If the designers of a class design bad boats, that class is a failure, if builders do not put in the best of work and workmanship the same applies, while if the rules are bad the class is bad, and these three things affect the owner, for he owns the result. The rule makers spoilt the large class in 1897, and it was not until 1920 that it was strong again, when the rule makers again encouraged vessels similar to the old *Britannia*.

Now the rule for the large class is the universal rule of America, for America has adopted the European rules for classes from 12 metres downwards, and we have adopted their rules for the largest class, the "J" Class, so that as the large racers are now designed to an international rule, their position is stronger than ever before.

Britannia's lines are wonderfully fair and sweet to the eye, and looking at them one ceases to wonder at the fact that even though forty years of age, she still is as fast as the best, for the sections, water-lines and buttocks could not be improved upon to-day. This is borne out by the plan of *Britannia*'s profile, quarter buttock, deck water-line and midship section, with that of *Enterprise* dotted on it, for in 1930, *Enterprise*, after defeating the best of the American cutters, defeated the best of the British, namely *Shamrock*, in the *America*'s cup contest. And the likeness between *Britannia*'s lines and those of *Enterprise* is very startling. I have brought *Enterprise* to *Britannia*'s size for comparison, for it must be remembered that *Enterprise* is 7 ft. shorter on the water-line, being 80 ft. on the line.

This plan, while showing that great minds think alike, is also a great tribute to the brain of G. L. Watson, for besides showing that his lines can hardly

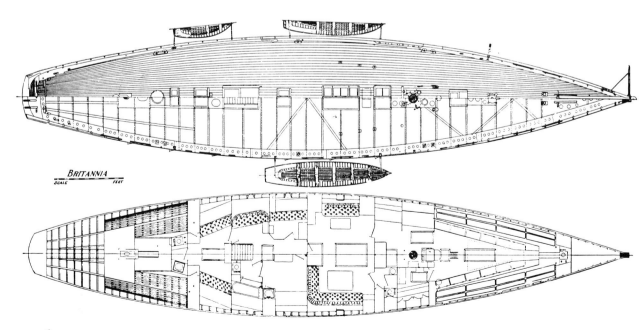

be improved upon to-day, it proves that the proportions and shape he gave *Britannia* are considered ideal after all these years, for it must be remembered that he did not have to consider quarter beam, length, displacement and draught, as the designers of to-day are forced to do. But when these restrictions were added to the rating rules they encouraged practically the same hull as *Britannia*'s.

Her accommodation plan shows that half of the accommodation length is given over to the crew and the galley.

Next abaft of this is her saloon, which, extending the whole width of *Britannia*, is spacious and airy, and is most cheerful with its pictures. Farther aft, abreast each other, are two state rooms, the owner's being to starboard, and in this the dressing-table is the most noticeable thing. For in its two upper corners are carvings showing thistles, roses and shamrocks all flourishing on one stem, pointing out that Scotland, England and Ireland should for each other's benefit dwell together in unity and peace, while in the two lower corners are the most striking carvings of all, Britannia with her shield and trident. How well the carver loved his work, and the hours spent at it one can only imagine, for this age, with its acceptance of articles stamped out by machines in thousands, has lost one of the greatest joys of life—the joy of working quietly with the hands and brain alone.

Right aft of the accommodation is the ladies' cabin, separated from the rest of the accommodation by the companionway and bathroom. The counter, as in almost all the large racers, is used as a sail locker, and although roomy there is need for all this space as the sails are large and their area makes them heavy to handle.

The thin counter, looked at in profile, appears too weak to stand up to the strains put upon it by the mainsheet and the backstays, but inside it is carefully braced by a light but well thought out steel girder throughout its length.

The sail plan shows her original rig, with the Jack yard topsail and reefing topmast in dotted lines, and in solid lines the Bermuda sail plan given her in 1931. The noticeable thing is the increased height and reduced base of the sail plan.

Her gaff with all the halyards and blocks attached to it is gone, and her mainsail has now a parabolic curve from truck to boom, whereas before it was flattened at the gaff, and the topsail on one tack was flattened as it was pressed against the peak halyards. So, with the saving of weight aloft and the increased efficiency of the mainsail, *Britannia* is far better to windward now than she was. But as so often is the case in this world, a gain in one direction is a loss in another, and it will be some years before the tall Bermudian rig on these large cutters will be properly understood, and until such time we shall not see *Britannia* able to storm across Channel at 12 knots in a nasty sea as she did in 1893 against the American *Navahoe*.

And those who, like myself, sigh over the loss in hard weather ability must be patient, and remember that in *Britannia*'s early days the large cutters sometimes carried away their short mainmasts, which showed that they were not properly understood then, so the time will come when these tall Bermudian spars will be as strong or stronger than the old short gaff cutter mainmasts, for with increasing years comes increased knowledge and improved materials.

May that time come soon, for these large cutters are sturdy and strong, and fit for any weather in every detail excepting in their masting and rigging, and when the day dawns that sees their one weakness strengthened every lover of the sea will rejoice.

Apart from the royal aura attending her, which so impressed the general public, *Britannia* was a most interesting vessel from the technical angle. Born of a long out-dated Rule, she was competitive in the "J" Class forty years on— which suggests that a good boat is a good boat, no matter what the whims of the Rule-makers may dictate.

Her deep bulwarks were removed, the long tiller, handled with relieving lines and tackles, gave place to wheel-steering, the great jack-yard topsail was replaced with bermudian rig; but *Britannia* sailed on and on, to win hundreds of races. I once had a clutch of tall white sails over near the Island shore pointed out to me: "See that one second from the right?—that's the King's yacht!" As a small boy, I was disappointed in their stately progress, though I dare say they were moving quite well, for I felt that a racing yacht ought to flash across the horizon like a shooting star.

For years after that, Cowes Week photos of King George V in his round sailor cap, like the one worn by a "blue-jacket" in the Navy, were a familiar sight in the newspapers. And when he died *Britannia* was given a Viking funeral. Not for her the slow decay in some sleazy knacker's yard, she was towed out to the back of the Wight and sunk in deep water—a fitting grave for such a grand old lady.

International 14-footers

The International 14-foot Dinghy Class is, without doubt, the most popular of all classes, for the YRA dinghy committee founded its rules on solid rock, as they took the rules of the three most popular dinghy classes, the West of England Conference, the Norfolk and the Small Boat Racing Association, and boiled these down into one set of rules, making the National, which afterwards became the International 14-foot Dinghy Class.

Pengelley designed and built the crack dinghies that founded the old West of England Conference Dinghy Class, producing excellent little boats. He might be called the father of the thought, for succeeding designers in after years picked up the threads where he had left off.

slow up very much when heeled, for the U-bow section is circular where it is affected by the water, and her sections throughout are generally speaking the bottom halves of circles, and even to-day after an active and successful life of twenty-three years *Snark* is still able to win races, especially on days when the winds are puffy, and it is impossible for a dinghy to be sailed along perfectly upright all the time. Her sail plan is the Gunter lug rig, for the old rules of the class would not allow any spar to exceed the boat's length by more than 18 in., and this rig was the nearest approach to the present Bermudian rig. To-day *Snark* has a rig very like that shown in *Avenger*'s sail plan. The construction and arrangement is little altered even to-day, for it is practically identical with to-day's practice. It will be seen that all the weight and gear is in the middle third of the dinghy and the only advancement in all these

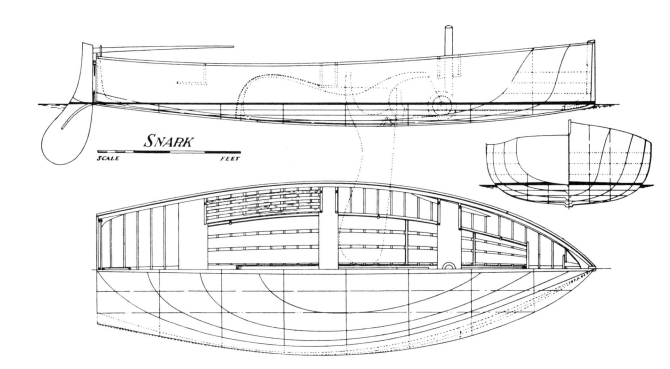

Snark, designed and built by Morgan Giles, shows the excellency in design and build reached by the West of England Conference Class in 1911, and the fact that in 1929 this boat, when owned and steered by Mrs Richardson, was sixth in the Prince of Wales' Cup Race at Plymouth shows how well thought out the National Dinghy Rules were, for they enabled a dinghy eighteen years old to race with every chance of victory. In that race there were thirty-five starters, most of the dinghies being only two or three years of age and many only two or three months.

The lines of *Snark* are those of a boat that will not

years is the tendency to concentrate the weights more and more amidships, for although a boat can be trimmed to her design water-line by the weights spread throughout her length, she is not so fast. In a seaway however small the waves the bow must rise easily and sweetly, and so must the stern, otherwise the two ends tend to dig in, when the bow pushes more water than it should or the stern drags water after it, and it is only by putting the weights amidships that the liveliness in the ends can be obtained.

And *Avenger* shows we have hardly improved upon *Snark*'s arrangement of weights, as she left little room

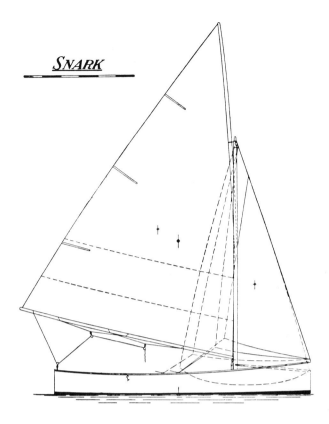

Snark

for improvement.

When some six years ago I started in to design dinghies the problem was difficult, for Giles as a designer was king of the castle and in a very strong position, having, in twenty years or more, developed and perfected the *Snark* type of lines. If I followed, it was obvious that I would always do so, and so I decided to go off on another tack. One of the maxims of racing is that when last do something different, and this was comforting and helpful.

During my apprenticeship I had worked a great deal on fast motor-boats, hydroplanes and flying machines, and these fast craft went all out for the V section, for while at speed this lifted, a U section tended to bury, but the thing against the V section was that while in power vessels it was ideal, it was not for sailing, as they were often at large angle of heel.

And *Avenger*'s lines show how this V section was carried out, and it was successful, for although when heeled it was slower than the *Snark* type of sections, when upright it was faster with a far higher speed off the wind, due to its lifting tendency, which made it plane easily and so jump from the limited speeds of displacement vessels into the almost unlimited speed of hydroplanes. How successful this V section was can be gauged by *Avenger*'s string of prize flags, 52 firsts, 2 seconds and 3 thirds, out of 57 starts. And she was never beaten in strong winds—but she had to be sailed upright at all times excepting in a strong calm when she was listed just enough for the sails to drop naturally into their proper shape, so that the gentle air of a strong calm had not to push the sail at all into its shape, all of its energy being then saved for pushing *Avenger*, and the speeds reached in a strong or a fresh calm were so slow that the shape of the underwater did not matter.

Her arrangement shows the weights concentrated as much amidships as possible, the mast is well in from the bow to keep her lively forward, and all the seats are amidships, for Tim (my crew) and I sat as close as possible together either side of the midship thwart, which, besides keeping the ends lively, had the advantage that two men together offer no more windage than one, and when at close quarters and cross tacking to escape from another dinghy I had only to nudge Tim in the ribs and we were about without a murmur, while the other dinghies called, "Lee, oh!" every time they tacked.

The only times I called "Lee, oh" were when we were actually not tacking, for after cross tacking to escape from another dinghy's dirty wind, say eight times, we almost always escaped easily by my saying "Lee, ho" in an agitated voice, shooting head to wind and then going back to our existing tack, by which time the other man was about and having no way could not tack immediately on us. And almost always once *Avenger* had her wind clear to windward, she left the

49

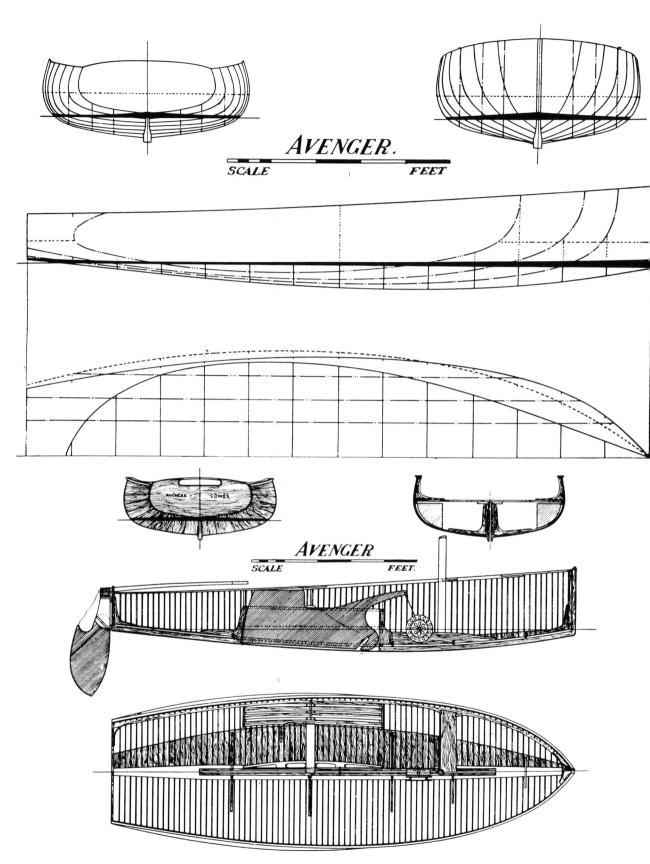

AVENGER.

SCALE   FEET

AVENGER

SCALE   FEET.

fleet. Her buoyancy tanks are fitted in each bilge amidships, and so keep the water shipped out of the lee bilge, where it takes all the life out of a dinghy, making her sluggish, unstable and slow.

Avenger's lines, sail plan and construction plans shows the present-day dinghies, for her successful season showed the advantage of the V section, and other designers were forced to develop this type of design, and broadly the only difference between the *Avenger* and the *Snark* is in the sections, *Snark* being U sectioned and *Avenger* V, for generally speaking the construction and arrangement are the same. *Avenger's* rig shows the two cross-tree and double diamond rigging which keeps all cross-trees and rigging close to the mast, and enables the jib to be sheeted in clear outside everything. In the years to come all larger racing vessels will probably have similar systems of rigging, for the larger classes take years to adopt the more highly developed rigs of the smaller classes. It must be so, for there is the cost of experiment, a dinghy mast costs no more than the cross-tree of the large cutters, and added to this is the time of making a mast, and the wonder is that the large classes are so well advanced as they are, so the keenest and most popular small class (which at present is the dinghy) will always be the leaders in thought, with the larger classes following in its footsteps according to size.

To illustrate: the 12-metres at one time had two headsails, they now have one; the large classes had three headsails, some now have only two, and future years will see them with but one headsail, in spite of the difficulty in sheeting down such a sail, for winches will overcome this.

In the dinghies we know that to let our boats heel is to slow them, and some years hence all larger classes will discover this simple truth, and they will be sailed as a small boat by the main sheet, which will be arranged and led to a winch so that one man can play it in and out for the puffs of wind just as he would a heavy fighting fish on a rod.

Sailing a dinghy well in strong winds calls for a great deal of anticipation and understanding. The wind is always untrue in strength and direction, varying all the while, be it ever so little in direction it is enough to make a great deal of difference to an observant helmsman, who takes advantage of it, for with a freeing puff he luffs and, whenever headed, goes about and lays closer on the other tack. The ever varying strength of the wind is looked after by the main sheet, for when racing a vessel is canvassed to suit the lulls in the wind, while cruising she is reefed to suit the squalls, so a racer is always over-canvassed in the squalls, and then her main sheet should be eased until she has no more weight in her sails than she can bear. The

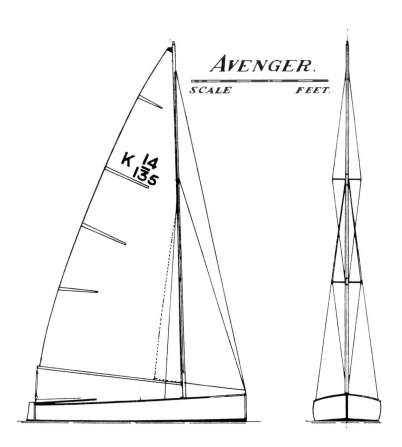

AVENGER.

SCALE   FEET.

K 14
135

Daring, *with Uffa sailing, and* Pintail. *Both Uffa designs,
they were first and second in the 1929 POW Cup race.*

photograph of *Avenger* shows her tearing along at her
top speed with her mainsail eased away, so that only a
few feet at the clew are doing any work. The playing of
her mainsheet won her many races, for often she would
leave other dinghies standing with her mainsail eased
off and flying out to leeward like a flag, while they had
theirs full of wind, the difference being that they were
heeled over and lifeless while *Avenger* was upright and
footing fast. I am a cruising and not a racing man, and
excepting for the year in which I raced *Avenger* have
averaged under twelve races a season. My reason for
pointing this out is to stress the importance of playing
the mainsheet in and out in strong winds, which are
always squally, for it has enabled a cruiser like myself to
win races from purely racing men, and in the keenest

class in this or any other country, for with over 300
boats in one class and as many as 50 in a race,
competition becomes keen and races hard to win. The
helmsmen are scattered all over Britain, and the best
from each district travel hundreds of miles every
summer to take part in the Prince of Wales' Cup, so the
winner has to beat the best helmsmen in the country.

So generally speaking the best and keenest helmsmen in Britain are in the 14-ft. class, which is
developed more than any other class, and so all other
classes do, or should look to it for ideas. Their rig at
present is some years in advance of other classes.

All because a dinghy mast costs no more than a
large cutter's cross-tree, and in the event of the mast
falling down there is no danger to life and limb on a

dinghy as there is with the larger vessel. This is illustrated forcibly by the difference in weights of the mainsails; a dinghy's mainsail weighs 5 lb. and *Britannia*'s mainsail weighs three-quarters of a ton.

The difference in the mainsail weights represents the difference in the designer's problems, and because of this great difference the small boat designer is generally in advance of the designer of large vessels, not because his ideas are more advanced, but because he can carry them out so easily and cheaply, and so for some years the racing classes of Britain will follow the ideas of the 14-footers, the leaders in thought.

Do the thousands of people now sailing planing dinghies acknowledge their debt to Uffa? I doubt it. The V-bottom section later made possible the hard-chine plywood dinghy. This in turn initiated all the do-it-yourself building from a kit. Thousands of modern glass-fibre dinghies are the same shape as their plywood hard-chine ancestors. They had to be so, to bridge the gap, while classes were composed of both plywood and glass-fibre boats. Now, the shape goes on, although the modern material does not enforce it. All of this stems from Uffa's basic principle of a V-section as opposed to a U-section for the bottom. Likewise, all modern techniques of dinghy sailing—toe-straps and then trapezes—derive from his conception of holding the boat upright at all times, so that she would plane over the surface of the water, instead of heeling over and ploughing through it.

Winning the Canoe Championship of America

On February 25, 1933, the Royal Canoe Club held its annual dinner and presentation of cups, and as winner of the two most important of these, it was my privilege and pleasure to fill them and pass them round the table. In olden times, many a man met his end by being stabbed from behind whilst drinking, and often in old pictures a man is shown drinking with his back to the wall. This protected him from behind, and the old tankards had glass bottoms, so that those drinking could see any danger ahead. As the challenge and De Quincey Cups were passed round, three men stood all the while, the man drinking toasted the man on his left, while the man on his right, who drank last, remained standing, so the man drinking had a friend standing either side of him as was the old custom.

Through dinner we toasted canoeists the world over, and afterwards Roger and I departed, he to Oxford and I to the Isle of Wight, hoping that we should both take canoes to America in August, sister ships that would not only conform to the American rules, but also to the English.

Two days later, on Monday, I sent the following cable to a friend, who is the oldest canoeist in America:

W. P. STEPHENS, 3716 Bay Street, Bayside, New York.

Please send 1933 sailing canoe building rules, latest date for Challenge from England and date of Contest. UFFA.

Letters and cables passed between America and England, mostly cables from England, with the result that we challenged for everything we could, Roger as the Royal Canoe Club, and I the Humber Yawl Club.

Then came the designing of our canoes, Roger helping with letters, full of ideas, from Trinity, and finally the canoes were designed to both sets of rules.

The American maximum beam rule forced us to design canoes 3 in. narrower than the English rule,

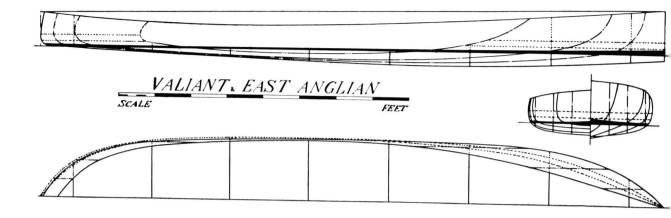

VALIANT & EAST ANGLIAN

SCALE   FEET

whilst the English rule, demanding a ¼ in. planking, forced our hulls 40 lb. over the minimum weight allowed in America.

Time alone would tell if we could afford to give away the 3 in. of beam under the English rule, where no sliding seat was allowed, and carry the extra 40 lb. of hull weight round the American courses, but we thought we might, and it was worth trying.

The rig would have to be different, as entirely different rules prevailed. Under the American rule, we were allowed 111 sq. ft. of sail, actual area, with a height of 16 ft., but no side stays on the mast, while under the English rule we were allowed 96 sq. ft., YRA measurement, with no restriction as to height or staying of mast.

The Americans had no limit to the depth of centre board, so, while racing there, we thought we would try a very deep one, which was impossible under the English rule, which only allowed a board to extend 1 metre below the canoe. The American rules allowed a sliding seat, and the English did not, so by changing rigs and drop keels, and adding a sliding seat, our canoes were changed from the English to the American rules.

The American rule allowing a sliding seat, but no sidestays, made a fair amount of work calculating the leverage and power exerted by a man five foot out on a slide, plus the power of the canoe and balancing this against the strength and elasticity of hollow spruce spars. For, to win races, weight, and so strength, must be cut down to its limit, yet to carry away a spar is fatal.

After the designing, came the building. *Valiant* and *East Anglian* were built upside down, for the bottom of any vessel is the part that decides her speed, and by building upside down this is always in view.

Moulds were made and set up on the stock, the keel, stem and stern post fitted, and the moulds ribbanded out. Next, the ⅜ in. by ¼ in. timbers were steamed and bent 2 in. apart round the ribbands, and the first skin, of ⅛ in. thick diagonal planking, fitted. Oiled silk, stretched over the diagonals, formed the next skin, on which the ⅛ in. fore and aft planking was fitted and

fastened. After this the keel case, extending almost the full length of the canoe, was fitted, followed by the deck beams and mast steps, and after six coats of varnish inside, the deck, of specially made 3-ply, was fitted, and fastened in one piece.

We had had some experience with the English rig, but none with the American, so this was the first to be tried out, and it proved better to windward than expected, and I easily beat an International Star Class Yacht to windward in both light and strong winds, so, as far as windward work went, we were contented with our canoes, for winning, after allowing the Star Class 15 minutes in an hour, showed this to be a good rig.

Then the English rig was fitted in a tabernacle, which allowed the mast to be reefed in strong winds. This too seemed good.

In Long Island Sound

The morning of the final race was just what the doctor had ordered for us, as a strong wind was blowing from exactly the same quarter as the day before, and we imagined we should be sent round the triangle the same way, but as we approached the committee boat, running dead before the wind, we were surprised to see the signals hoisted for the course the opposite way round. So we started with a dead run to the lee mark, with no chance of a windward leg, unless the wind shifted. *East Anglian* led over the line and then started her attempt to hinder *Loon* and *Mermaid* hoping to get *Valiant* away, but as *Valiant* rounded the lee mark, her foresail gybed round and fouled her foremast, and so she was practically hove-to. *East Anglian* then fought *Loon* and *Mermaid*, and soon won first place, leaving Roger astern. However, he soon had *Valiant* sailing again, catching *Mermaid* and then *Loon*, but instead of coming on ahead into first place, while I dropped back to the enemy, he stayed with them, and, attacking *Loon*, refused to come on. Roger in *Valiant* was doing such a good job with the foe, that I in *East Anglian* sailed, reaching and running round the course quite happily, until there came a heavy shower of rain at the end of the second round,

54

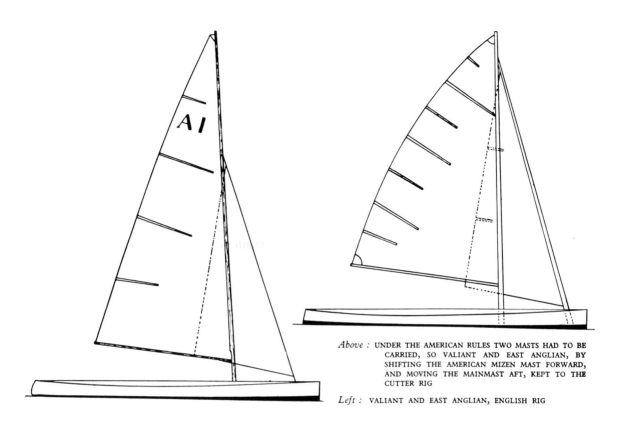

Above : UNDER THE AMERICAN RULES TWO MASTS HAD TO BE CARRIED, SO VALIANT AND EAST ANGLIAN, BY SHIFTING THE AMERICAN MIZEN MAST FORWARD, AND MOVING THE MAINMAST AFT, KEPT TO THE CUTTER RIG

Left : VALIANT AND EAST ANGLIAN, ENGLISH RIG

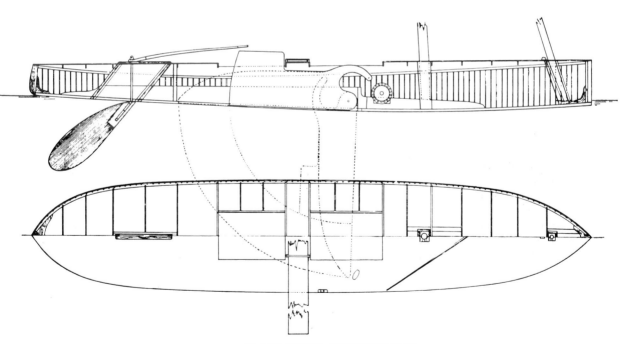

VALIANT AND EAST ANGLIAN, CONSTRUCTION PLANS

Uffa's favourite picture: sailing an International class canoe.
This one was Gallant, *the first he designed and built after the*
American and British sailing canoe rules were united.

which knocked the wind down to almost a calm. Then the pace slowed, and Roger had to fight very hard to keep the now faster *Loon* back, but he held her until the wind freshened again at the end of the third lap and all was well once more. On the last lap, after rounding the leeward mark, the wind shifted a little, making the close reach to the weather mark possible with sheets slightly eased. So *East Anglian* romped down this reach, and *Loon*, rounding the leemark behind *Valiant*, tacked at once to starboard. Roger, although he could easily lay the weather mark, swung about with *Loon* and it was not until a motor yacht, under way, put *Loon* about, that Roger came round with him. Then they both reached with sheets well off for the weather mark, round which *East Anglian* had already passed to reach across the line and win, thanks to her team mate's aggressiveness.

So the International Canoe Trophy came to England for a year, with the other canoe cups we had won from the Americans.

These were the fastest times of the three races, but as there was no windward work, the speed through the water was far below that of the previous day, 9 miles in $1\frac{1}{2}$ hours equals 6 knots.

So after 48 years, the canoe trophy left America, the first time it had ever been won from them during all those years.

Roger and I were very pleased and proud at having beaten the best canoe sailors of America on their own waters, but this joy was tempered with a strange sadness hard to define. They had welcomed and opened their hearts to us, taken us into their tents and homes, and we had been the best of friends before and throughout the races, and now that the races were over, were better friends if possible than before.

Only in adversity and defeat does real sportsmanship show up, as it is easy to smile after victory, yet when *East Anglian* swept across the line to win the deciding race for the International Trophy, such a shout of joy and noise of tooting went up from the yachts witnessing the race, that I felt a lump rise in my throat. For here were Roger and I, strangers in a strange land receiving cheers that could not have been louder had they been given for Leo Friede and Walter Busch.

And so our canoe races in America ended enjoyably. They had been marked by clean sailing with no protest, or the need for one, throughout, and this added greatly to the pleasure the races had given us.

A few days later the International Canoe Trophy was presented at the New York Athletic Club, by William P. Stephens, and a challenge read out immediately afterwards. Roger and I said we should like to give them a trophy for their canoe racing to show how grateful we were for all their kindness. We suggested a model of *East Anglian* and *Valiant* to be given for a nine mile race on the triangle.

Two days later four cups left America in the *Olympic* with Roger. These cups had never before, in their 48 years' history, been won from America. The International Trophy, the National Sailing Championship, the National Paddling and Sailing Combined Championship, and the Paul Butler Trophy were to sojourn in England for a year.

Roger and I had enjoyed our visit, for we had met in America canoe sailors who had filled us with

"The stern joy which warriors feel
In Foemen worthy of their steel."

It was a successful foray into American waters. Uffa and Roger De Quincey brought back cups for the International Canoe Trophy, the National Sailing Championship, the National Paddling and Sailing Combined Championship, and the Paul Butler Trophy, all of which had been held in America for 48 years. After the idyllic period camping on Sugar Island in the St. Lawrence river they teamed up with Rolf Armstrong, who was already carrying his own canoe on the top of his car, and Uffa bought an old clapped-out trailer on which they trailed *Valiant* and *East Anglian* down through New York State to Bayside for a further series of races. Cars were not like those of today, and what with the trailer collapsing repeatedly, it must have been quite a drive. New sails were made for them by the American branch of Ratsey because the ones they had brought were 11 square feet under area.

Whirlwind

Owner, George M. Pynchon
Designer, L. Francis Herreshoff
Builder, George Lawley & Co.

LOA 130 ft. 0 in.
LWL 86 ft. 0 in.
Beam 21 ft. 9 in.
Draught 15 ft. 6 in.
Displacement 159 tons
Sail area 7,535 sq. ft.

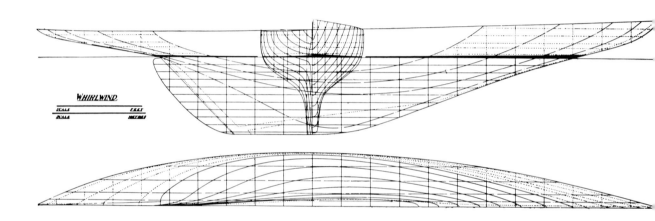

Whirlwind was the last of the four "J" class yachts to be ordered in 1929, and for this reason her designer chose composite construction for her, as the very limited number of workmen trained in light plating for yachts were already absorbed by the other three "J's," *Enterprise, Weetamoe* and *Yankee*; and so, as *Whirlwind's* construction is very similar to that of *Britannia*, she should last as long as the royal cutter, which is still racing under our king's burgee after a long life of forty-two years. But *Whirlwind* has in her construction one great advantage over *Britannia*, and that is in her main keel taking the lead (ballast) keel, for the main keel is a bronze casting, which will not shrink, swell or rot, so that, if the Yacht Racing Rulers govern well and wisely, we shall still see *Whirlwind* racing fifty years hence. If they do not she will probably be cruising then, for she was designed with hatch openings, etc., reinforced to Lloyds requirements, so that she could easily be converted into a cruiser, these hatch openings being used as cockpits for racing.

She has no centreboard as her lateral plane was considered to be sufficient without.

LINES

The lines show the hull designed for the weather off Newport, which is generally a moderate wind, with quite a choppy ground swell, and excepting for her wider deck aft (designed by request) she is very similar to *Istalina*, the crack racer in the "M" class, also by Francis Herreshoff.

The profile is very pleasing to the eye, the stem sweeping down to the keel in a very sweet line, and to a man who, like myself, believes that a pointed stern is a logical ending for all vessels, her stern is a joy to behold. The bow water-lines and sections are snubbed in sharply, due to the fact that the profile has been hollowed out to save wetted surface and water-line measurement, while the load water-line aft and the water-lines above show how she has been snubbed in there.

The buttocks are very easy, though the one very close to the centre line at first sight appears steep and unfair. This is caused by the fact that the lead keel is stream-lined, and is very wide forward of midships, and it must be remembered that this buttock is cutting

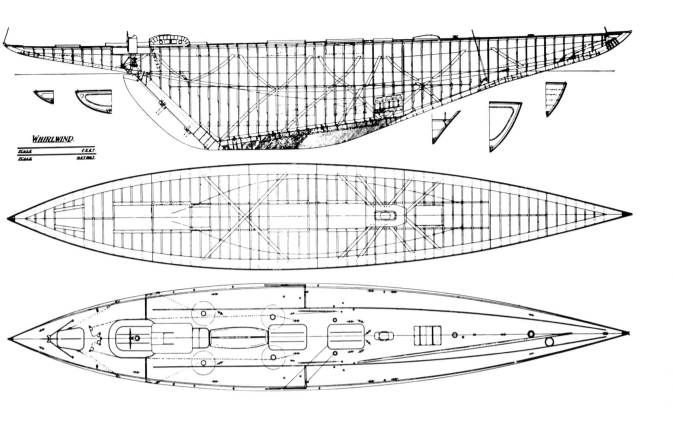

WHIRLWIND.

the sections at such a fine angle as to be almost useless in fairing *Whirlwind*, and little notice should be taken of this line.

The sections themselves are very pleasing, being easy and yet powerful, and *Whirlwind*'s lines throughout are a joy to those who understand.

CONSTRUCTION

Of the fifty-six plans included in *Whirlwind*'s design there is only room for four in this book. The one showing her construction is the general plan, many of the unusual features being covered by detailed plans, the main keel of bronze being an example of this. From her construction plan it will be seen that this keel is made up of five pieces, all of which are bolted together with angled flanges, which extend downwards as well as up, making a strong T-shaped joint. Through her length she has five sets of diagonal strap bracings, these connecting to the bilge stringer plate before continuing on their way to the keel from the deck.

The planking is in two skins, the total thickness being $2\frac{1}{2}$ in., so that *Whirlwind* is not liable to shrink, and even if she did water could not find its way through her double planking, as it would through a single skinned vessel.

Her deck is in two thicknesses, these being laid diagonally and measuring all told $2\frac{1}{4}$ in. It is covered with 10 oz. canvas, and this deck has three sets of diagonal bracings, two at the mast and one amidships, in addition to the deck beams and fore and aft tie plates.

SAIL PLAN

Whirlwind's sail plan is worthy of study, for she came out with the double headsail rig, which all the "J" class racers have since adopted, but because it was so unusual and ahead of its time *Whirlwind*'s managers were afraid to use it enough to get used to it. And so this rig teaches us all the great lesson that once any pioneer has put his hand to the plough he should not look back or even pause, but continue with his work until he has reaped the harvest. Molesworth, a great engineering friend of mine, produced the 6-wheeled motor car and was awarded a certificate for its fine performance at an exhibition in 1906, but not until his patents had lapsed, a few years ago, did all the manufacturers recognise the advantage of six wheels for many jobs. So a pioneer must remember always that he is ahead of his time, that he must fight and overcome his difficulties alone and unaided until he has perfected them before he will receive any help from his fellow men. Even to-day after all the "J's" have more or less copied *Whirlwind*'s rig it is still in advance of them, for the forestay is only one-third of the base of the fore triangle away from the mast, which shows this rig to be far more daring than at first sight one would suppose, as it is not only an attempt to change from a three headsail rig to a two, but an effort to go the whole way, and in one step change from the triple headsail rig of the past fifty years to the single headsail rig of the future. For that staysail is so small that its stay is in effect the midstay, which has often been found

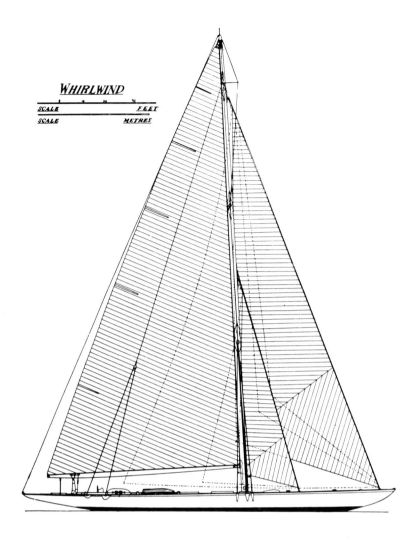

WHIRLWIND

SCALE   FEET
SCALE   METRES

necessary with the single headsail rigs of 6-metre and other racing classes, this stay having been found useful in stopping the mast from sagging aft halfway between the jib halyards and the deck.

It will be noticed that no stay comes aft from the mast where this fore (or mid) stay joins it, and when in the years to come the large racers such as *Whirlwind* finally adopt the single headsail rig it will not at first differ very much from this sail plan now already six years old.

Time, too, will, I think, see the "J's" getting longer and more powerful, for *Whirlwind* with her greater length and displacement is more suited to the heavier mast (5,500 lb.) and heavier accommodation (7 tons) that the newer rules have wisely insisted upon for all "J" class racers.

If you have ever encountered a Twelve Metre, at close quarters, while afloat, you may recall the sheer size of the thing, the feeling of immense power in the sails, and the suction of her passing, which left your own craft rolled upright with sails shaking. Compare, then, the dimensions of a "Twelve" with those of a "J" and you begin to get an inkling of the grandeur of their progress, and with what majesty they moved. From on shore, I watched them afar, racing in the Solent, without realizing that I witnessed an historic spectacle, then fading, and never to be repeated. Later, on the Hamble River, I knew well the hulls of *Endeavour* and *Velsheda* lying in their mud berths. I went aboard *Velsheda* when Norman Vine, a Lloyd's surveyor, first converted her for use as a houseboat. She was then in quite good shape—not long after the War. From time to time, stories appear in the Press of someone about to fit out the old ship to sail across the Atlantic; but I will believe it when I see it actually happen.

In another part of this book Uffa rants on, at some length, about what he calls weak "maidenly" rigs set above good seaworthy hulls. Well, yes; but designers and engineers were still only beginning to grapple with the problems of bermudian rig, which everyone mistrusted at first, and in any case at this size the problems were formidable.

Giralda

Owner, James R. Piper
Designer, James R. Piper
Builder, James R. Piper

LOA 86 ft. 0 in.
LWL 85 ft. 0 in.
Beam 18 ft. 6 in.
Draught 5 ft. 0 in.
Displacement 150 tons
Sail area 3,000 sq. ft.

The beauty and charm of a barge is hard to define. To watch one sailing along serenely and silently at about 3 knots in a light breeze is to feel a sense of peace and quiet joy steal over one. Their black hulls and tanned sails fitting in with any landscape, natural or artificial, combined with their stateliness of movement, gives to them a beauty which can only be approached by few things on this earth.

Added to this is the fact that everything about a barge has a purpose in life, and having been developed to fulfil that purpose for so many years is practically perfect, and so has a beauty of its own that perfection alone can give.

Giralda is probably the best example of a sailing barge, for, built and launched in 1897, she won the diamond jubilee championship and continued winning the championship of the Thames for many years, being champion for 1897, 1898, 1899, and 1900. She continued winning at intervals until the outbreak of the War in 1914.

Her designer and builder, James R. Piper, kindly loaned me the model from which she was built, and from this model I took off the lines, which appear now for the first time. They are very interesting, as they show that although designed to carry 100 tons or so of freight in narrow shallow creeks, or across the open sea, *Giralda* has very sweet and fair fore and aft lines.

Her buttocks are remarkable, for we must bear in mind that a barge, for stability and carrying power, has a box section amidships, and that in spite of this *Giralda*'s buttocks are clean and fair, and show that she has a wonderfully clean run. The water-lines are easy, and are very fine under water aft, these explaining the gradual and easy change from the round bow section to the square section amidships and the triangular shaped transom aft. The perfect blending of the round bow, the square midship, and the triangular aft sections is the work of a master of his craft, for there is no doubt that James Piper is a past master in the art of building barges.

When *Giralda* was built her designer offered her command to Harry Munns, who was the crack barge skipper of that time (1897), but Harry, after looking the barge over, declared that she would never win a race, and declined the command.

So another skipper took her and won everything for four years running. This reminds me that the barge I used to sail in (it seems hundreds of years ago now) flew a cock on her mizen, as she had won races on the Thames, and in spite of old age was still able to beat everything in her line on the Solent. After one brush with a very fine barge skipper the following incident happened.

He dropped his hook near us, and getting in his dinghy sculled her round our bow (we call sculling, rowing with one oar over the stern, the oar making a figure eight in the water all the while) and after looking at the bow he said, "I'm —— if I can see why she sails so well." To which our skipper replied, "You're looking at the wrong end; it's the stern of a ship that counts."

This is so, always has been, and always will be; the old French designers knew this, that is why their fighting and fishing vessels have always been faster than ours, and I have been very successful as a designer through paying more attention to the stern of a design than the bow.

I believe that could Harry Munns have seen *Giralda*'s buttocks he would have accepted the command of her, and then probably she would have won even more championships than she did, though she won so many.

Loaded to the line shown on the plan her displacement is 150 tons, though only drawing 5 ft. of water, and this gives an idea of the usefulness of a barge, for it means that it can go practically anywhere the tide flows, up narrow creeks to unload and load at the quay there, or across oceans. Two of James Piper's barges have proved this by sailing across to South America, where they worked for many years, one taking 104 days and the other 99 days to sail from Greenwich to the River Plate.

It would be difficult indeed to evolve a more efficient sailing craft than the spritty barge. She can be, and is, handled by two men only, she can and does carry 100 or so tons of cargo, she can and has sailed across oceans, she can and does sail and work her way up narrow winding and shallow creeks, for her topmast houses and her mast tumbles aft, and is lowered by her forestay, so that she can pass under bridges, and she can steal along in a light air, or storm along at some 10 knots before a gale of wind. And yet in spite of all these virtues no more are being built, and probably half of those now trading have an engine in them. Millions of pounds have been spent in research work and the development of engines, and it seems to me that if anything like the sum had been spent on, and the brains of so many engineers had been applied to, sailing vessels, they would still hold their place in this commercialised world of ours. Instead of this, however, nothing was done to forward the sailing vessel once engines came into being, so the sailing vessel has marked time, while the power ship has developed in an amazing manner, and has practically

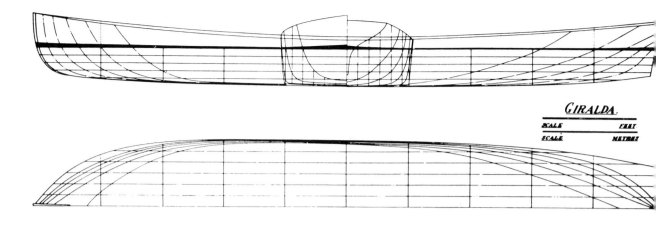

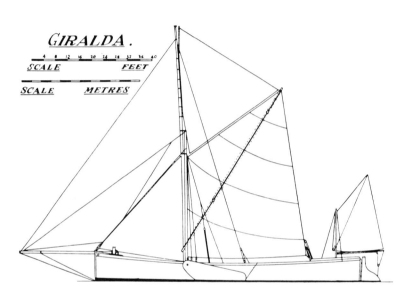

GIRALDA.

4 8 12 16 20 24 28 32 36 40

SCALE   FEET

SCALE   METRES

ousted the sailing ship as a work vessel all over the world, these barges being the most vigorous of our once large and active merchant fleet of sailing ships.

The sail plan shows that the topsail stows aloft on the topmast, for it has hoops just as the schooners have that fish on the banks of Newfoundland. The mainsail, it will be seen, is brailed up by four brails, and so is the mizen though using a smaller number of brails, the staysail and jibs alone lower and stow on the deck, and this is the reason two men can handle a barge. Their large sails, mainsail and topsail, stow aloft, and so save a great deal of energy and time.

The leeboard shown in the sail plan enables a barge to work to windward. It is swung on its fore end, and lifted or lowered by its aft end.

The idea of the mizen sheet leading to the rudder is that, as the rudder is swung across her stern in tacking, it takes the mizen with it, and this swings her stern across until the staysail is aback (it is held aweather until she is about and then let draw) so the barge has to

stay, for rudder and sails swing her on her leeboards. A barge seems a great big vessel when in a narrow creek or river, for she sails into places others shun as impossible. I well remember in one very narrow place, we tacked perhaps six times without gaining a yard, and the skipper did not mind a bit. "The great thing to remember," he said, "is keep moving; all the time the water is flowing past, we have full control, but once it stops, it means that we have, and so have lost control of our ship." Soon after a free puff let us through that narrow part with the wind ahead, and all was peace and quiet again, no rattling of sails and blocks; they were all asleep on the wing as we slid silently along. In reefing at sea it is far easier if one man at the helm can keep the vessel just moving without much weight of wind in the sails, for that gives control of the ship, and keeps the sails and blocks asleep and harmless.

Such a vessel as *Giralda* would make a very fine floating home, for in her man could change his neighbourhood and neighbours whenever he wished, he could enjoy the fresh air and sunshine all the year, and so live a peaceful and happy life.

It seems that yachtsmen alone will keep alive the art of sailing a barge, just as they do the art of sailing generally; but it may not be so, for a large firm, wondering if sailing barges could solve their transport problems, approached me, and I said I hoped and believed that they would.

So we are at work on the problem, and time alone will tell if we think they will, and if we are right to think so, for if we do think so there will be a fleet of about 100 built, which will add to the beauty of shores as they pass to and fro with their cargoes.

If this cannot be, then we must turn up photographs of the vessels who traded under sail, and live upon our memories, and amongst these will be barges such as *Giralda*, for she fits in so well with any landscape or mood.

Two thousand or more sailing barges once worked the Thames Estuary and the East Coast ports or rounded the Foreland to go down Channel. When London's traffic was horse-drawn much of the fodder and straw was moved into the city this way. The "stackie" barges, when their capacious holds were full, had an immense hay-rick reared up above the coamings. The mainsail was brailed up enough to clear it and a man atop the stack directed the helmsman, who could see nothing ahead of him. Yet with all this top-hamper, and extra windage, they were still manoeuvred under sail along narrow creeks and waterways.

When I kept a sailing dinghy on the Itchen River, at Southampton, in the early Thirties, the big steel-built barges of the Blue Circle Portland Cement Company used a wharf there. They carried the Blue Circle insignia on the topsail. I encountered one beating up through a narrow reach of the river at half-tide with little more than two ship's lengths on each tack. As a very novice sailor, I approached in some trepidation; but I was lucky and managed to duck under her stern as she pulled away from my side of the channel.

Fifteen spritsail barges went to Dunkirk to help pull out what remained of the British Expeditionary Force. *Ethel Everard* and *Royalty*, laden with ammunition, blew up, and six others were never heard of again. *Glenway, Ena, Pudge, Thyra, Tollesbury, H.A.C.*, and *Spurgeon* survived. Lieutenant Heron and eight French soldiers found a leaky 14 ft. boat and set out for England. In the mist they sighted a big barge and hailed her. In the hold were about 250 French soldiers, resting after eight days and nights of incessant bombing. When they had made sail, Lieutenant Heron took the wheel, grounded on a sandbank, got off on the rising tide, and they were away into the mist, picking up more survivors in open boats. Late in the evening they saw three armed trawlers, and when the fog lifted to show the white cliffs of Dover about a mile away, the heavily laden barge was towed by them in there.

A few years after the war I served on a passenger steamer plying along the lower Thames and across to the French coast. There was still a sprinkling of barges on the river then. We would sometimes see one or two brought up waiting for the tide to serve, just above Sheerness. Once, on our lay-off day, at Gravesend, I watched a barge put about just off our berth. About twenty minutes later, when she was out of sight, another came dropping down on the tide and put about in exactly the same spot. With those conditions of wind and tide that was the place to go on the other tack. This should be remembered when making comparisons between commercial seamen and yachtsmen. The professionals are doing the same thing every day of their working lives, while yachtsmen are more often than not bumbling their way into a place they have never seen before.

In the late Fifties *Sirdar* came round from the Thames for Cowes Week and I met her running up through the West Solent setting a huge spinnaker—a sail she would never have used when she was a working barge.

The last real working barge was Bob Roberts' *Cambria*. I met him once, at the Boat Show in London—by no means the rough-talking barge skipper, quite suave and sophisticated, but determined to make *Cambria* go on earning her living under sail.

The barges which survive now are mostly kept for racing. A few, owned by big firms, are used to entertain business contacts, or have their holds fitted out as showrooms for trade goods.

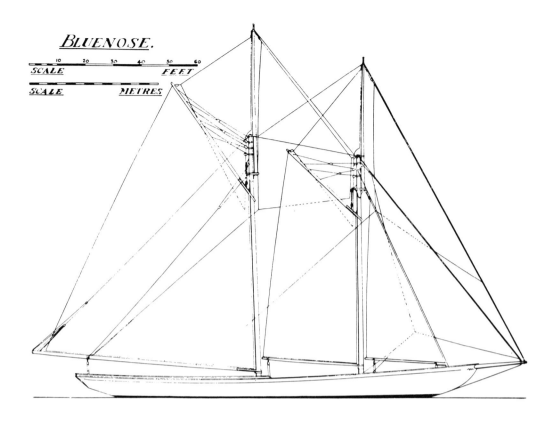

BLUENOSE.

SCALE   FEET

SCALE   METRES

Bluenose

Owner and Skipper, Angus Walters
Designer, W. J. Roue
Builder, Smith and Rhuland

LOA 143 ft. 0 in.
LWL 112 ft. 0 in.
Beam 27 ft. 0 in.
Draught 15 ft. 10 in.
Displacement 285 tons
Sail area 10,000 sq. ft.

In 1920 the two cutters, *Resolute* and *Shamrock IV*, both refused to race one day when it was blowing 30 miles an hour, and this led to the international races for deep sea fishing schooners off Halifax that October, for the fishermen were very scornful.

The first series of races was won by the American schooner *Esperanto* of Gloucester, who defeated the *Delewana* of Lunenburg, representing Nova Scotia.

Though defeated, the Nova Scotians were not dismayed; they went to W. J. Roue, their greatest designer, and asked him to design a fishing schooner to uphold their honour as a maritime province, and it was pointed out to him that the vessel must also be a good carrier, and one that would pay as a fisherman, as well as be able to run a cargo of cured fish to the West Indies or to Europe. The hold must be large enough for 4,200 qtls. of 112 lbs. each, and *Bluenose* is the average size for the work intended.

The deed of gift for these international races insists that the construction and rigging must be as used in fishing vessels generally, the idea being to race fishing schooners that could pay their way, and not fast inside ballasted yachts.

The difference between the Gloucestermen and the schooners from Novia Scotia is that the Gloucestermen carry smaller cargoes of fresh fish into their home ports, while the Nova Scotian salts hers down, and carries a heavier cargo to more distant ports. In looking at the plans of *Bluenose*, therefore, we must remember that first of all she must pay as a fisherman, then pay as a freighter and after that hope to be fast enough to beat the best American fishing schooners.

The schooners that fish summer and winter on the Banks of Newfoundland have to be, as well as weatherly and seaworthy, easily handled, for though *Bluenose* has a crew of twenty-one, sixteen of them are dorymen, which means that there are only five left aboard when fishing, and one of these is her cook. Only by remembering all the conflicting points can we really appreciate the design and build of *Bluenose*.

Her lines reveal her easy entrance and long clean run, and one is struck by the fairness of her easy water-lines, buttocks and diagonals, for we must bear in mind that *Bluenose* is first and foremost a work boat.

The overhangs each end are moderate and well balanced, and with their reserve buoyancy are a great help in a seaway. The sections show her high bilge, and it will be noticed that her floor has a rise of about 45 degrees aft. Generally in looking at the lines one is impressed by the way the designer has blended every requirement into a perfect set of lines.

The perfection of her lines may be gauged by the fact that *Bluenose* won the International Trophy for fishing schooners in the October of 1921, and has held it ever since against the Americans, who have challenged for it with some very fine schooners.

Her keel is 12 in. sided, and her stem and sternpost having the same siding ensures that she is to the standard construction for fishermen. Her frames are doubled, 9 in. × 10 in., spaced 27 in. apart, and as will be seen from the plan she is practically solid. To these frames her 4 in. thick planking is fastened, the ceiling inside being 4 in. thick as well, so it will be seen that

Bluenose is well and truly built.

Her rudder stock is 14 in. in diameter, for *Bluenose* through her career has often had to fight hard for her very life in a winter gale with the shoals, upon which she fishes, dead to leeward.

Her deck beams are 9 in. × 9 in., and to these her 4 in. thick deck is fastened. All these figures give an idea of the massive construction of the schooners that fish on the Grand Banks.

For sea work the schooner rig is, I think, best. The masts are stayed together so the rig is strong, and also the different sail combinations enable a schooner to handle well in any weather from a calm to a gale. For these two reasons the schooner is my favourite rig for off-shore sailing.

Though her mainmast is 20 in. in diameter it does not look at all large, neither does the foremast, which is 19 in. diameter, while both topmasts look in keeping with the rest of her rig, these tapering from 11 in. at the heel to 8½ in. at their heads.

Bluenose

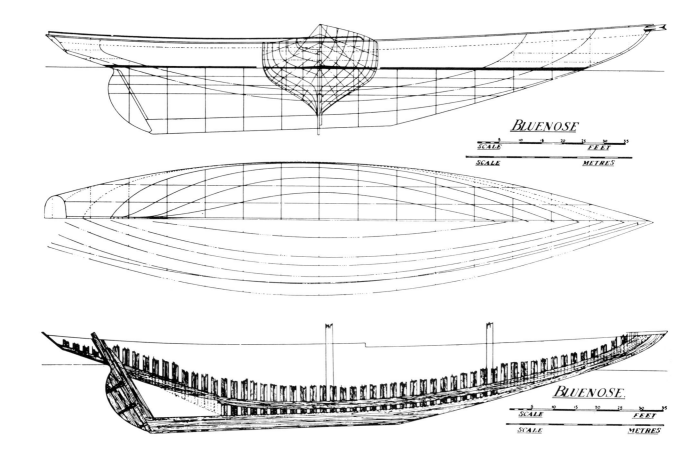

BLUENOSE

SCALE   5   10   15   20   25   30   35   FEET

SCALE   METRES

BLUENOSE.

SCALE   5   10   15   20   25   30   35   FEET

SCALE   METRES

There is something about a schooner, and when she is of these dimensions then she becomes a noble vessel indeed. All the fittings and deck-gear for *Bluenose* were robust, as befits a ship to fish the North Atlantic in winter off fog-wreathed Newfoundland. Her stacks of dories nested one inside the other with their portable thwarts removed, in the customary way of the Banks fishermen. The same system was employed by the big schooners which went over from Portugal.

When I was in Barbados in 1950 the big inter-Colonial schooners, like the *Francis W. Smith* and the *Marion B. Wolfe*, still ran from there down to Georgetown, British Guyana, on the South American mainland. Some had been built for this trade and some were "Bankers". Unlike the smaller inter-island schooners, they were run very efficiently, in big-ship fashion. The officers were mostly Dutchmen from the island of Saba—in khaki-drill tropical uniform. With a good Trade Wind on the beam these schooners could make the run in very fast time. They carried some passengers, as well as freight. It was one of the last commercial sailing-ship routes in the world. I will never forget seeing them moving out of Carlisle Bay, so stately, almost regal, under all that great cloud of canvas.

Stormy Weather

Owner, Philip le Boutillier
Designer, Olin Stephens
Builder, Henry B. Nevins

LOA 53 ft. 11 in.
LWL 39 ft. 8 in.
Beam 12 ft. 6 in.
Draught 7 ft. 11 in.
Displacement 20 tons
Sail area 1,300 sq. ft.

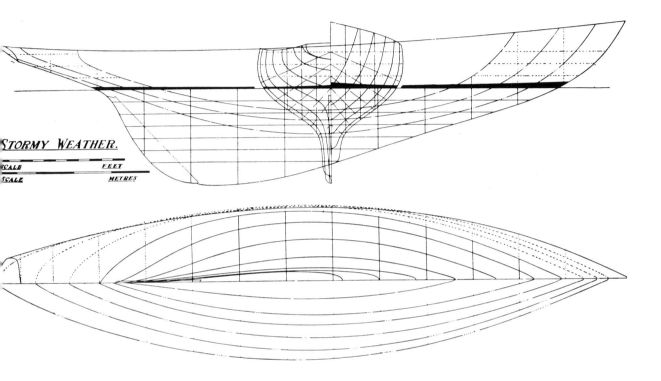

STORMY WEATHER.

SCALE — FEET
SCALE — METRES

There is no doubt that *Stormy Weather* is a remarkable vessel, that her crew understand her and all her little ways, and that she is built to stand the hard driving she has to endure, and so a study of her will prove profitable, for there is much to be learnt from her.

Stormy Weather is one of Olin Stephens' favourite designs, and her lines show her to be beamy and powerful, yet very easily driven, and therefore fast. She has moderate overhangs, and is exactly the type of vessel favoured by the new American rule for Ocean Racing, a type that should gladden the hearts of those who go down to the sea in such small ships.

Her diagonals are very fair and sweet, and her buttocks have that easy sweep that speaks of speed easily attained and maintained. *Stormy Weather* should glide along with the effortless grace of a bird soaring through the air, totally different to the clumsy, brutal

way in which the "wholesome, sturdy cruiser" smashes her way along at half *Stormy Weather*'s speed.

The sections show her high, easy, yet powerful bilge, which tells of easiness in a seaway, for though *Stormy Weather* will sail fairly upright she will not be stiff and jerky in her movements. The water-lines, it will be noticed, are sharp at their fore ends above and at the load water-line, gradually getting fuller as they get lower, until the lowest, through the lead keel, is virtually a true streamline.

The raking rudder is a method of cutting away wetted surface without interfering to any extend with steadiness on the helm in a seaway. If we look at French fishing vessels, tunnymen or crabbers, we see almost always a rudder with about 45 degrees of rake, and we must remember that while these French fishermen are designed for the sea they have always been far faster

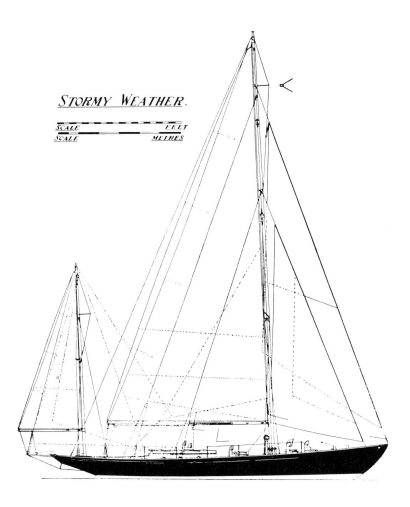

STORMY WEATHER.

SCALE   FEET

SCALE   METRES

than our own fishing vessels, without any loss in seaworthiness.

So it is with *Stormy Weather*, for she is faster than most cruisers, without any loss in comfort or sea-worthiness, and she is a fine example of Olin Stephens' designing ability.

The sail plan is very similar to that of the successful *Dorade*, by the same designer, the difference being that in the case of *Stormy Weather* Olin has moved the forestay inboard from the stemhead 3 ft. 6 in., giving her more than double the clearance between the jib and forestays. Aboard *Dorade* it was difficult to pass the genoa jib between these two stays when tacking.

Stormy Weather has a pair of jumper struts and stays, at the upper end of her jibstay, and, by doing away with the topmast stay to the stemhead and putting all the weight of the rig upon the headstays, these enable them to stand. Also, they enable *Stormy Weather* to dispense with her runners aft, except in strong winds. The runners holding up the fore- and jibstays are farther aft of the mast than the stays are forward of it, and so are well able to look after the strains on the stays and keep them bar taut. It will be noticed that the backstay is

permanent, leading to the counter, down past the mizen gooseneck.

The mainsail has a very good aspect ratio, for the luff is 58 ft., while the foot is only 25 ft. 8 in., giving a luff that is more than twice the length of the foot. A sail largely depends upon its aspect ratio for its efficiency to windward.

The mizen is a tiny little sail—no larger than a 14-footer's mainsail—as it has but 127 sq. ft. in it, but it is free by the rule that gives an allowance to a yawl. The mizen staysail, that reaches (as it should) to the deckhouse half-way along the main boom, is also free, and as at sea the mizen and mizen staysail might be useful, they are well worth their place.

The sail plan shows the wonderful assortment of headsails carried by *Stormy Weather*, as she has seven of these, ranging from her tiny storm staysail to her ballooner, which reaches half-way along the main boom—sails that will enable her to sail at her best in any weight of wind from a calm to a gale.

The mainsail has two 7 ft. 6 in. reefs, and also a 4 ft. balance reef, the latter being for use when running in a seaway, as it not only lifts the outer end of the main boom 4 ft. and prevents it tripping in the sea, but also, by flattening the sail, it stops rolling to a great extent. Such things show how wise an owner is to go to a good designer who is also a seaman. Then, and then only, does he get a vessel that is happy at sea.

Repeating the dazzling success of *Dorade*, *Stormy Weather* won the 1935 Transatlantic, while on this side she won the Fastnet, and then made the windward passage back to America across the North Atlantic in 24½ days—clipping two days off *Dorade*'s time. It was becoming difficult to dispute Olin Stephens' pre-eminence as a designer—or his brother Rod's as a skipper. British yachtsmen were left breathless. Had these two established a working arrangement with the "Wizard of Oz"?

Even today, studying *Stormy Weather*'s lines produces a pleasurable feeling. An art student does not proceed very far with his studies of the nude before he discovers that the human form consists of a series of curves in every direction. So with *Stormy Weather*. The symmetry is unbroken—everywhere.

Bermudian rig with hollow spars was now entirely practical; but required rather elaborate staying—including those two lots of runners on the main mast. The track was bolted on, instead of being fastened with screws, at the point reached by the head of the mainsail, where it would be with a single, and with a double, reef—and for the head of the trysail.

The V-drive for the engine is a surprisingly modern touch; but, from personal experience of it, I must say going astern with the screw out to one side like this is just "anybody's guess". However, we must recognize that the auxiliary engine was of secondary importance aboard *Stormy Weather*.

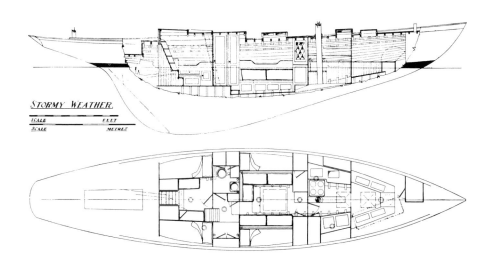

STORMY WEATHER.

SCALE   FEET
SCALE   METRES

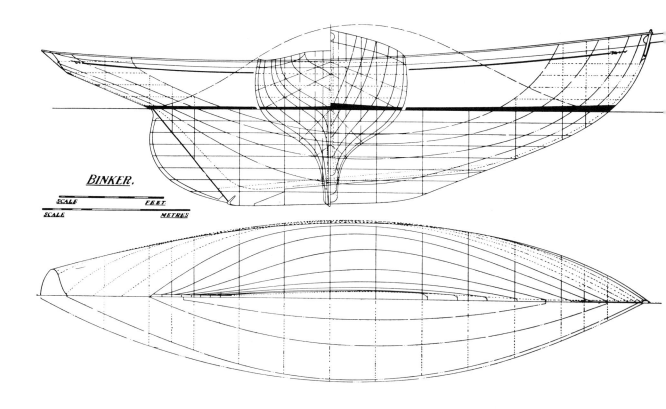

BINKER.

SCALE   FEET

SCALE   METRES

Binker

Owner, Boyd Donaldson
Designers, Burgess and Donaldson
Builder, Julius Peterson

LOA 39 ft. 10 in.
LWL 30 ft. 0 in.
Beam 10 ft. 0 in.
Draught 6 ft. 2 in.
Displacement (22,200 lb.) 9.9 tons.
Sail area 901 sq. ft.

When the head of a firm of yacht designers sets his gang to work on the plans for his ideal craft the result is sure to be interesting and instructive, and when that vessel is a development of another nation's fishing boat then she is even more interesting. For *Binker* springs from the old Itchen Ferry type fishing boat, as her pedigree will show.

In 1907 Arthur Payne designed the 25 ft. cutter *Scamp*, and as would be expected she proved very fast and able, for the Itchen Ferry boats themselves were noted for their speed, and *Scamp* was developed from them. Then in 1930 Ernest Ratsey had *Golliwog* built in America, she being an enlarged *Scamp*, and from her *Binker* sprung, the rigs of the two boats being practically interchangeable, *Binker*'s owner having in mind a boat in which he and his 15-year-old son could cruise in comfort and yet be fast to windward.

LINES

The lines show an easily-driven and powerful hull, while her deep forefoot giving a long lateral plane ensures her being steady if a trifle slow on the helm. The rather deep draught (as compared with her great-grand-parents who on this length would only draw 5 ft.) gives her weatherliness, and if this deep draught and the overhangs is ignored the family likeness between this little vessel and her ancestors 3,000 miles away on the Solent is clearly seen. The bow sections are very sharp and easy, while the counter is well V'd two points that make for quietness in cruising, for the flat stern given to most vessels smacks and pounds down on the waves when at anchor, with the result that little peace is found aboard at anchor unless the weather is very calm and the water smooth.

CONSTRUCTION

Binker is strongly built, her $1\frac{1}{8}$ in. thick planking being fastened to $2\frac{1}{2}$ in. $\times$ $2\frac{1}{8}$ in. steam bent timbers which are spaced 12 in. apart, all her fastenings being of bronze. Her lead keel (8,250 lb.) is held on by eleven $\frac{7}{8}$ in. diameter bolts and five $\frac{3}{4}$ in. diameter bolts, so there is little fear of this falling off.

She has a bilge stringer $6\frac{1}{8}$ in. $\times$ $1\frac{1}{2}$ in., tapered to $4\frac{1}{2}$ in. $\times$ $1\frac{1}{2}$ in., at the bow and stern, running throughout her length. Besides this she has diagonal strap bracings in way of the mast of tobin bronze $3\frac{1}{2}$ in. wide and $\frac{3}{32}$ in. thick, so it will be seen that the hull is well and truly built.

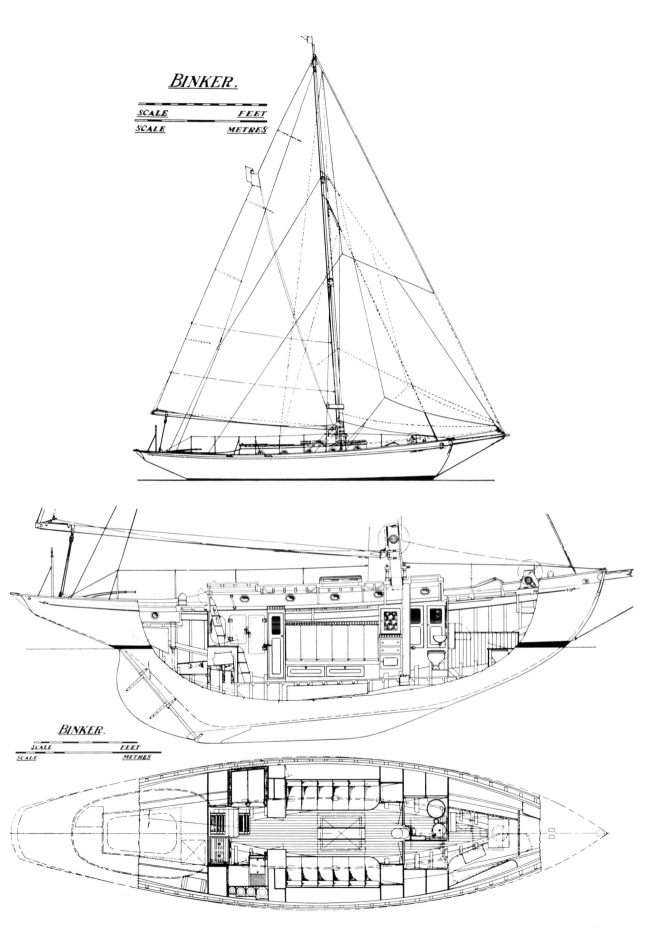

BINKER.

SCALE   FEET

SCALE   METRES

BINKER.

SCALE   FEET

SCALE   METRES

71

The deck plan shows no less than forty-two knees without counting the breasthook and quarter-knees, and so although the practice of stepping the mast down through the coach roof does not find favour on this, the lee side of the Atlantic, it will be seen that when they (as they generally do) step the mast through the raised deck in America it is done with a full knowledge of the stresses and strains set up by a mast, and that these are all looked after.

ACCOMMODATION

The accommodation designed for the particular requirements of the owner has the advantage of making this small boat seem very roomy, for from the mast to the cockpit there is no bulkhead across *Binker* at all, the cabin leading straight into the galley and ice chest aft. In the fo'c'sle is a single pipe cot to starboard and a sail bin to port, and between these two a folding wash-basin and a WC so arranged that they do not take any room away from the fo'c'sle.

On the starboard side the fo'c'sle extends aft to the mast, but to port the owner's washroom, entered from the cabin, has been cut out. In olden days the fo'c'sle was generally reckoned to go far enough aft to take in the mast, but now with the engine aft taking the owner's accommodation, and the smaller crews needed aboard our more easily handled boats it is seldom that the fo'c'sle has the mast.

The main cabin starting with the mast has a sideboard on each side forward, and then a long folding berth each side, the cushions of which it will be noted are divided into six, so that any one will lift and give access to the locker under or behind, without disturbing the whole seat or back as is usually the case.

At the after end of the cabin is the galley with the stove, dresser and sink to starboard, and the large ice chest to port. This galley is in the best possible place for small vessels, for here the motion is least, as it is near the centre of the see-saw, and also the fumes of cooking go straight out, added to which meals can be handed straight into the cabin or out in the cockpit according to where they are to be eaten, which largely depends on the weather.

Binker has a very large cockpit, and underneath this is her engine room, and fuel tanks, shut off from the rest of the accommodation as they should be. The 4-cylinder Gray motor drives a 15 in. propeller which leads through the port quarter 18 in. below the water-line.

The bilge pump is let into the cockpit floor, the suction leading down to the lowest point, which is under the galley floor.

The counter stern gives *Binker* a larger and more comfortable cockpit and afterdeck than most small cruisers of her type, though it is not long enough to take a permanent topmast backstay.

I must confess I find the connection with Itchen Ferry boats tenuous. However, a trained naval architect, which Uffa was, may see it differently. The knees shown in the construction drawing are interesting. They took immense pains to ensure that the hull was strong. Masts rising through the coach roof became commonplace later. The fo'c'sle lay-out suggests that a paid hand will be carried. Again, we are struck by the paucity of berths for the length; but that is how things were then. We see here the beginning of the life-line around the deck. Even when I crossed the Atlantic in 1949 it was still only a single wire covered in rubber tubing. This conferred the advantage that when coming alongside in a dinghy it was possible to crawl underneath. The addition of a second, lower wire put a stop to that.

Barnswallow

Owner, Paul Hammond
Designer, Starling Burgess
Builder, Paul Hammond

LOA 39 ft. 0 in.
LWL 30 ft. 0 in.
Beam, outside 10 ft. 6 in.
Draft, extreme 5 ft. 0 in.
Displacement 9·8 tons
Sail area 585 sq. ft.

To appreciate a vessel a man must understand the idea behind her design and construction and also her pedigree, for generally to understand is to appreciate.

Barnswallow's pedigree is short, for she was based upon Elihu Root's *Dormouse*, a very successful 20 ft. water-line cruiser with a transom stern designed by Burgess, who endeavoured in her case to produce a shallow draft hull that would go to windward well without a centreboard. In fact, *Dormouse* went to windward in an astonishing manner, proving herself to be weatherly, well balanced and easily handled, so much so that *Barnswallow* is practically the same vessel stepped up 50 per cent., the water-line length increasing from 20 ft. to 30 ft., with the transom drawn out enough to take a permanent topmast backstay.

Burgess made one slight difference when he laid *Barnswallow* down in Paul Hammond's red barn, for he hollowed the water-lines slightly at their fore ends, this change being the result of some tank tests he had just completed for Commodore Vanderbilt.

So the idea behind *Barnswallow* is a shallow draft sailing vessel that will go to windward without a centreboard and be easy to handle; moreover, she is designed for single-handed work, with her halyards and even the anchor winch worked from the cockpit.

She was built in her owner's red barn twelve miles from the sea by his own boatbuilder and his own fair

and *Barnswallow*'s owner and master-builder must have spent many hours of contented contemplation strolling the hundred yards over the old mill grinding stones and under the apple trees between his dining-room and the red barn where his ideas quietly took form and finally became a vessel such as any man would be glad to own. *Barnswallow* took three years to build, as she was started in 1932 and launched October 6, 1934,

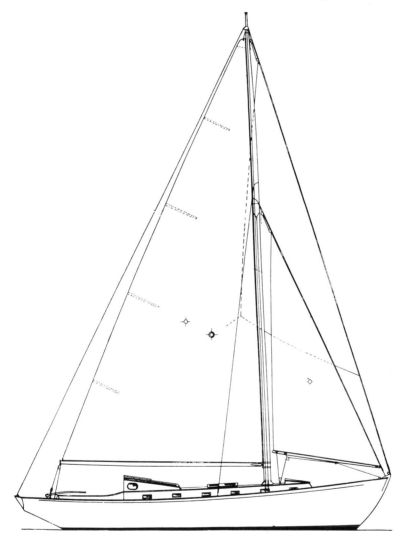

hands, with the help, during week-ends, of the off-shore crew of *Nina* and *Landfall*. Members of these crews will use her as a honeymoon ship as, one by one, Nature picks them off. Between whiles her owner and his Admiral sail her.

The joy her building gave her owner can easily be imagined, as there is no doubt man's greatest pleasure is in building. Even small boys love more than their other toys the bricks with which they build toy houses,

being built to the Herreshoff rule and surveyed by the American Bureau of Shipping.

Her lines at first sight appear heavy, for she is a vessel to be described as "all boat," but a further glance will show that the buttocks, water-lines and sections are all very easy, so that, for all her heavy look, she is very easily driven and so is a good sailing model. The fore ends of the water-line length line and water-lines below are shown as straight on the plan, for the hollow

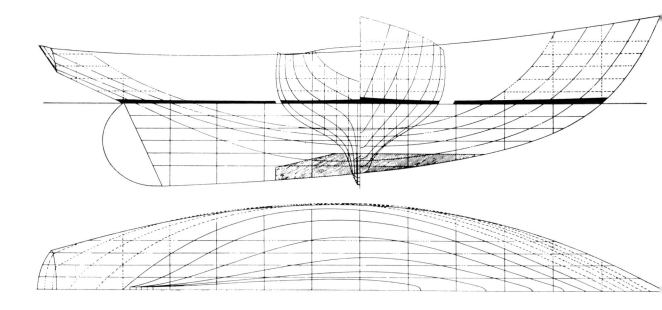

was not made until she was laid down full size in the red barn.

The total sail area is 585 sq. ft., of which 460 sq. ft. is in the mainsail, bringing this sail well within the strength of one man. The staysail works upon a horse, so, when sailing with these two set, there is nothing to tend when going about. All the standing and running rigging is of stainless steel, the shrouds and forestay leading through propeller stuffing boxes in the deck to the keel, thus taking the turnbuckles below deck and leaving it cleaner and clearer of things upon which sheets and light sails can catch, besides making a stronger system of rigging. There is no doubt that leading the shrouds to the heel relieves a vessel of much of the thrust of the mast, which is always trying to force itself through the bottom. Instead of splices, all the ends of the standing rigging are finished with soldered sockets, which give 100 per cent. strength as against the 85 per cent. strength of an ordinary splice.

All the halyards, which are of wire, lead aft to drum winches on the deck where they can be handled from the cockpit. Each winch winds up the entire halyard, so that there is no coil to stow or get adrift.

Even the roller reefing wire leads to the same place, so that a lady can lower the mainsail with her right hand and wind up reefs with her left. The staysail is on a roller with a furling spool at the head as well as at the tack, and these lines lead aft, so that the staysail, too, can be reefed from the cockpit. So that altogether *Barnswallow*'s rig is easily worked single-handed without any need for leaving the cockpit.

In such a boat as *Barnswallow* a man could sail into most of our old-world creeks, up to the old stone or wooden quay where, until the advent of the railway, sailing vessels loaded and unloaded coal, wheat, cattle, and, at times, contraband.

But now these creeks and quays are deserted and quiet, so that only such noises as the musical but insistent call of the redshank or the plaintive note of curlew can be heard; but in these lonely spots, watching wildfowl and birds about their daily tasks, a man can find peace and contentment such as is rarely to be found in this world. And happy is the man with such a vessel as *Barnswallow*, for in her he can escape the noise and uncleanness of large cities and sail into some peaceful old-world creek, or put out to sea, just as his mood takes him.

A yacht designed for the famous Paul Hammond incorporated some interesting ideas. She had an attractive interior, with the half bulkheads swept up round to the cabin roof in a semi-circle. It is a tempting thought to lead everything aft to the cockpit, so that all manoeuvres can be executed from there; but it seldom works out that way in practice—at least not in my experience. There always seems to come an unscheduled hectic dash forward to clear something which has fouled up. (It happens in yachts rigged normally, too; but at least you are expecting it!) Running the shrouds and forestay down through the deck in propeller stuffing boxes was cunning. Bottle-screws are a frequent cause of things getting fouled up. Latent in all rope is a propensity for flicking itself into a half-hitch fit to hold through all eternity at the very moment when this is least wanted. Having the bottle-screws below deck would hinder tuning-up the rigging, which could only be done by slacking off, or taking up, in accordance with shouted instructions from on deck.

Thetis

Owner, Mrs Affra Cross
Designer, Alfred Mylne
Builder, R. McAlister & Son

LOA 41 ft. 6 in.
LWL 26 ft. 9 in.
Beam 8 ft. 3 in.
Draught 6 ft. 6 in.
Displacement 7·5 tons
Sail area 1,126 sq. ft.

One of the most interesting of the smaller racers at Cowes was *Thetis*, for, designed by Alfred Mylne as long ago as 1904 (thirty-one years), she could beat the 8-metres day after day in the light weather that prevailed through the "Week," and won first prize practically every time she started in her class, which was the 10 to 30 ton handicap class.

Indeed, *Thetis* had such a winning way that I asked Alfred Mylne if she could appear in this book, and so we have here another design that proves that we have hardly advanced in hull design for the last forty years, a sad but indisputable fact, as a study of *Thetis* will confirm.

Her sections give a vivid idea of her sweet hull, for it will be seen that they combine speed, comfort and weatherlines in a wonderful way.

When we know that a yacht is getting on in years her constructional details interest us, for we know that

they must be good, and so a study of the scantling section of *Thetis* is worth while.

Her planking $\frac{7}{8}$ in. below water and $\frac{3}{4}$ in. above, is fastened to grown frames $2\frac{1}{2}$ in. $\times$ $1\frac{1}{2}$ in. at the heel and tapered to $1\frac{1}{2}$ in. $\times$ $1\frac{1}{2}$ in. at the head, spaced 2 ft. centres, and also is fastened to her bent timbers, $1\frac{1}{4}$ in. $\times$ 1 in. at the heel tapered 1 in. $\times$ 1 in. at the head, and as there are two of these between each grown frame, it is seen that the planking is strengthened and fastened every 8 in.

The frames are connected to the 6 in. wood keel by galvanised steel floors, and these take the $1\frac{1}{8}$ in. dia. lead keel bolts, and also the $\frac{3}{4}$ in. dia. wing bolts.

The deck beams are $2\frac{1}{2}$ in. $\times$ $1\frac{3}{8}$ in. with a 3 in. crop or round, and to these the $\frac{3}{4}$ in. thick tongued and grooved deck is fastened; as the deck is canvas covered, it does not get thinner as the years pass through scrubbing and scraping as an ordinary deck does. Very few owners realise how much is planed and scraped off their spars and decks every year, but an inspection will reveal the amount, for by looking near ironwork on spars and hatchways on decks, it is clearly seen that many a vessel has thinner spars and decks than supposed by owners, builders and designers, due to zealous scraping by her crew.

Thetis has a pipe cot in her fo'c'sle, and a single berth to starboard abreast the mast with a WC to port, and two berths in her main cabin, and this, with her cockpit, makes her a very comfortable little cruiser.

The sail plan shows the way her sail area is divided, for of her 1,126 sq. ft. of sail, 678 sq. ft. is in her

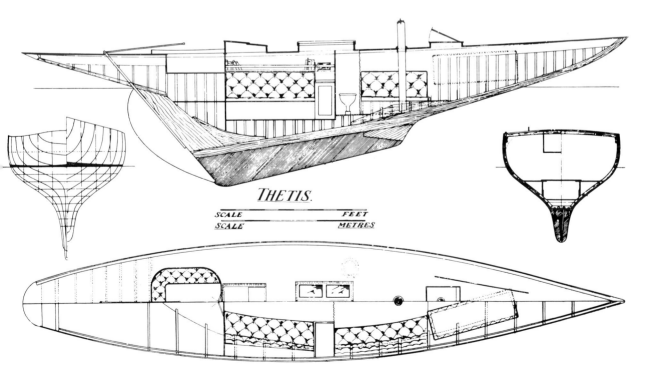

THETIS.

SCALE ——— FEET
SCALE ——— METRES

Thetis.

SCALE   FEET.

SCALE   METRES.

mainsail, 112 in her topsail, and the remaining 336 sq. ft. in her two headsails, and though this sail plan looks old fashioned, the record of *Thetis* on the Solent this year shows it to be a better rig than we imagine. It is astonishing how easily we are deceived. *Thetis* came to the Solent and has departed, but the handicappers still have no idea of the speed wrapped up in her hull, her old fashioned rig being their undoing, and as we go through life we find it hard to discern truth from falsehood more often than we realise.

Some years ago during the Clyde Fortnight we awoke to find an onshore breeze, at Hunter's Quay. It appeared to be blowing hard, actually it was blowing about 25 miles an hour only, but because we could not see the wind and could only hear it, it seemed much more with the waves dashing on the beach, each wave making a noise of its own, and so attempting to deceive the brain into thinking a gale of wind was blowing. A helmswoman there, in reply to a question by a friend of mine, said, "It is noisy, that's all."

And that summed it up exactly, and just the same remark could sum up our newspapers. I live so far away from any road that no one will deliver a newspaper to me, so I seldom see one. Now and then, when in London, I see a fine dashing poster, most exciting, one would imagine the world was about to

end; I buy the paper and find it is nothing but noise, and then feel thankful that I seldom see a newspaper. Ah me!

All these and many more thoughts are conjured up by the innocent look of *Thetis*, who so deceived the handicappers. She is fast and comfortable, and so worthy of close study.

It must have been fun to take a boat more than thirty years old and bring her in ahead of all the current crop of yachts in the Cowes Week racing. Alfred Mylne always had a formidable reputation as a designer, the forces of wind and wave are finite, only in the harnessing of them is there scope for progress, and increased speed of displacement sailing yachts over those of a previous generation can never be more than marginal. In the light weather of that year's Cowes Week *Thetis'* topsail probably helped. In strong winds, the story could have been different?

Zest

Owner, Roger de Quincey
Designer, Knud Reimers

LOA 27 ft. 8 in.
LWL 22 ft. 2 in.
Beam 6 ft. 3 in.
Draught, extreme 4 ft. 2 in.
Displacement 1·77 tons
Sail area 215½ sq. ft.

Zest is a very advanced type of cruiser, in fact, I should think she is the most advanced in the world, and so her type will not be looked upon with a favourable eye by most, for it takes years and years to break the habits and ideas that have grown and have been accepted by

squarely and so are of the greatest value to the builder for laying down and fairing up. Though she was only designed to these lines, it will be seen that the others are very sweet and fair as a result. The sections show her high, powerful yet easy bilge, which is actually above the water-line, and this it is that gives her the power to carry her tall mast and sail so well in spite of her easily driven hull.

The lead keel (925 kgs.), ·90 tons, is fastened by seven bolts.

Zest is built with two bent frames between her steel frames, a method of construction largely used but one which I do not greatly admire, preferring all wood or all metal construction. Even in an all wood constructed vessel I do not like mixing grown and bent frames, preferring all grown or all bent frames, so that the vessel is either rigid everywhere or pliable everywhere.

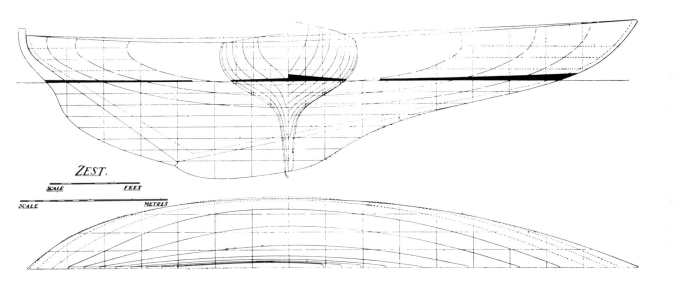

yachtsmen the world over. Their one great weakness lies in their not being able to grasp the fact that with increased knowledge of building come lighter and stronger hulls, which must therefore be given lighter displacements, otherwise the keels will be so heavy that these more lightly constructed boats will be uncomfortable at sea, for it must be borne in mind that all weight above that of the actual construction and equipment of a yacht goes into her ballast. As time goes on and this is realised there will come an acceptance of *Zest*'s type for cruisers, so that she, and vessels like her, will be looked upon as normal by all, instead of by the few disciples of light displacement.

Her characteristics are her very easy fore and aft lines, the water-lines and buttocks being very easy throughout. She, like all Knud Reimers' boats, was designed on diagonals, all of which cut the sections

The fo'c'sle is really only large enough to store things in, and here will be found dry storage for the best clothes, which only come out for great events ashore. In *Vigilant*, my 22 square metre, we stored our dinner jackets and stiff shirts in the bows, where they were prefectly happy, both going and returning from Sweden.

Abaft the fo'c'sle is the main cabin with a berth each side which has sitting up room, while farther aft is the galley and pantry, just under the coach roof. Next comes the cockpit, and aft in the stern is a small locker. This cockpit is a comfortable size, and the sampson post, taking the mainsheet in the middle, enables the helmsman to trim his mainsheet as well as his jib sheet while still looking forward, which is often a great help. *Zest*'s sail plan shows the modern tall narrow rig, for the mainsail luff is three times the length of the main boom. It will also be noticed that the jib carries out this tall and narrow idea, so that though she has only 215 sq. ft. of sail, *Zest* is remarkably fast, for the rig is as efficient as we can make it with our present-day knowledge and gear. Three times the base for the height of a sail is very close to the limit our sails will at present stand in the way of aspect ratio.

The forestay leads down through the deck to the main keel, where its strains can be taken easily, and the forestaysail tack hook is treated in the same way.

The mainsail is roller reefing, and until I visited Sweden I had never seen the combination of roller reefing and a tack tackle so well worked out.

Of the three headsails shown on the plan one reaches two-thirds along the main boom, and in this way *Zest* increases her sail area in light weather without increasing her spars, and there is no doubt that overlapping sails, because they increase the area in a few seconds without any increase in spars, should be carried by all cruisers and encouraged by racing classes, who, after all, find out what is good and bad for the cruising men, though cruising men do not realise or admit this.

Uffa's remark that the Tumlare was the ''most advanced'' design in the world showed acute perception. The sail plan would not be out of place on a light displacement ocean racer and even by modern standards the displacement of the Tumlare, at least as given here, is very light indeed. A modern boat would have more beam and freeboard, while the old garboard restraints due to wood construction are no longer seen. Of course, rudders have moved aft.

Tumlares and their larger sisters which had the same lines and rig proportions were used after World War 2 for ocean racing. Their success in this role swept away the old conception of heavily sparred pilot cutter types for ocean racing; developments of them were then designed to ocean racing rules. A number of Tumlare class yachts are still to be seen being sailed happily in the British Isles and Scandinavian waters.

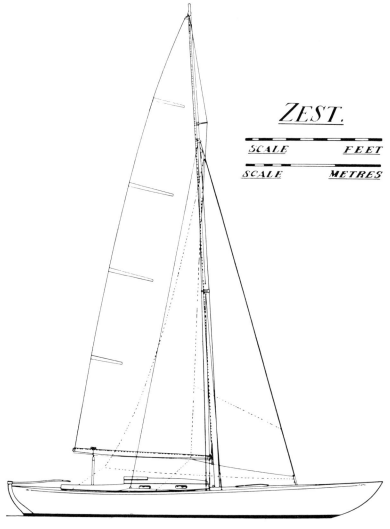

ZEST.

SCALE   FEET

SCALE   METRES

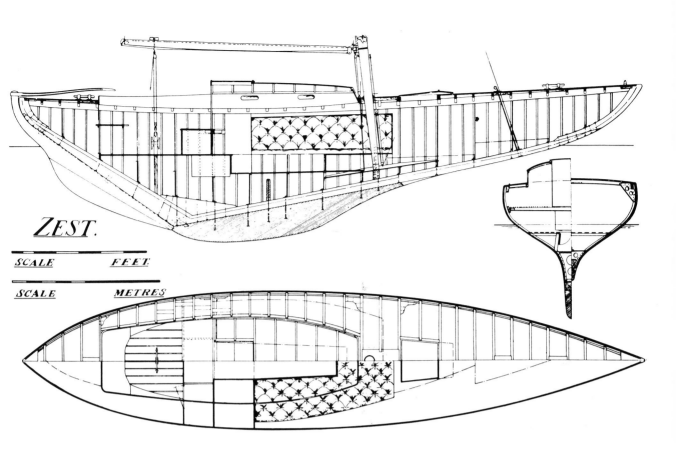

ZEST.

SCALE   FEET.

SCALE   METRES.

Emanuel

Owner, Commander R. D. Graham, RN
Designer, A. Anderson & Son
Builder, A. Anderson & Son

LOA 30 ft. 0 in.
LWL 25 ft. 0 in.
Beam 8 ft. 6 in.
Draught 5 ft. 0 in.
Displacement 8 tons
Sail area 475 sq. ft.

In this little ship her owner crossed the northern part of the North Atlantic single handed, an Atlantic peopled with cold grey seas, icebergs and fogs, yet in spite of all these the little *Emanuel* came to no harm till at the end

For an Atlantic crossing the *Emanuel* is small, but in her her owner had previously cruised as far south as Spain, and also northwards to Iceland, and so understood his ship, and there is no doubt that the gift of understanding is the greatest of gifts.

Her lines give an impression of a sturdy and yet fairly fast sailing cruiser with very short ends. The buttocks and diagonals are easy and fair throughout, and while the water-lines may appear to come in very suddenly aft, it must be remembered that such a vessel sails over the water, not through it, and so these water-lines do not count for much until she is heeled.

The sections are very good to look upon if we close our eyes to the corner where the garboard joins the built-on fin keel. This corner is for economy's sake, and it always seems such a pity to study economy to that extent, for *Emanuel* will last a great number of

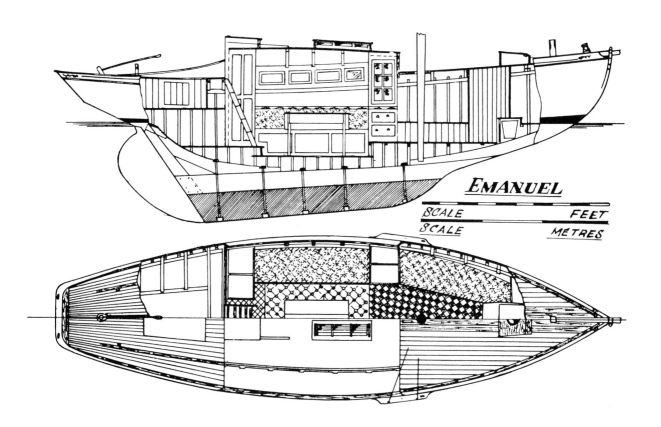

of her crossing, when her jib sheet carried away as her owner was attempting a narrow entrance in the dark. The strong wind then blowing immediately tore the jib to ribbons, and as his little vessel would not stay, her owner gybed her, and she hit the rocks to leeward, coming off, however, without any harm, after which he put to sea and safety, till the dawn of another day.

All of which stresses the importance of sound hulls and good gear.

years; she has already carried her owner safely over many thousands of miles of deep water, and when spread over the number of years she will enjoy, and the thousands of miles she will sail, such an economy seems futile. She is a perfect little ship, even to a critical designer, excepting for that little economy.

Her accommodation is increased to that of a larger cruiser by the fact that her cabin top sides extend to the ship's side, and this, as well as giving more room below, makes for a stronger hull and gives space on deck for stowing her 9 ft. dinghy, so is a threefold blessing.

It will be noticed that the galley occupies its rightful position for small cruisers, as it takes the after end of the saloon.

The problem of making a passage across the Atlantic in such a small craft is that of stowing gear, and of the vessel carrying the extra gear required for such a long passage, for all these little vessels when crossing oceans are loaded down below their designed lines, and it is just as well that the larger seas of the ocean are longer and kinder to them in proportion to their size than the smaller, steeper seas they usually encounter when cruising in strong tidal waters.

The Royal Cruising Club awarded this cruise their most coveted trophy, "The Royal Cruising Club Challenge Cup," and the following quiet and well balanced words by Claud Worth (one of our finest seamen) who was judge, and awarded the trophies in 1934, show that the RCC took everything into consideration and considered the awards from a seaman's viewpoint.

"Emanuel" (wrote Claude Worth, in the *RCC Journal*) "is a 7-ton cutter without auxiliary power. Commander Graham planned to sail from Falmouth to Newfoundland. After a fruitless search for a companion he decided to sail alone rather than give up the venture.

"On May 19, *Emanuel* left Falmouth and three days later arrived in Baltimore after a rather rough passage. Already running gear had begun carrying away, which it continued to do at intervals throughout the voyage. Commander Graham tells us that he started with his old gear in order to save the new rope for the Newfoundland coast—a rather dangerous economy, and the frequent repairs must have been exhausting for a lone hand. On May 26, *Emanuel* took her departure from Mizen Head and the Bull Rock. When possible, the vessel was made to steer herself with the helm lashed. Being single-handed greatly increases the risk of such a voyage. Once, when the yacht was running with helm lashed and the owner asleep, there arose a strong wind and a big sea, and a wave crest washed on board, waking him in time to see that the yacht was running too fast for safety. The mainsail was furled and two warps towed astern and she drove to the NW safely at about 2 to 3 knots. Crossing the Labrador current the air was bitterly cold, there was much fog, and icebergs were sighted. St. John's, Newfoundland, was reached on June 19. After a few days' rest Commander Graham cruised on the Labrador coast, where he nearly came to grief owing to the jib sheet carrying away.

"The news that *Emanuel* had been sailed single-handed from England to Newfoundland at first caused some misgiving. The Club is for the encouragement of good seamanship and legitimate enterprise, but

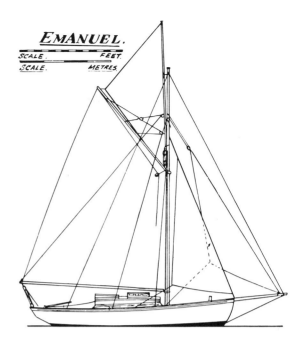

EMANUEL.

SCALE. FEET.
SCALE. METRES

recklessness is not regarded with favour. But Commander Graham had proved himself and his vessel in cruises to Spain, the Faroe Islands, and elsewhere. I am satisfied that, having failed to find a companion, he was justified in sailing alone if he wished to do so, and that the voyage was undertaken with adequate knowledge and solely for the love of adventure at sea. It was a remarkable achievement, quite different from a similar voyage in the warm and steady trade-wind zone."

When Claude Worth wrote thus, the single-handed crossing of the Atlantic was a rare feat—particularly by this cold northerly route. No self-steering gear aided the lone mariner on his way. He had no radio transmitter to scream for help if things went wrong. He sailed out into the wastes of the Atlantic, and either he arrived at the other side—or he didn't. No sponsors financed him. He paid for everything himself. Commander Graham was not the first yachtsman to cross an ocean successfully and then very nearly wreck his ship on the other shore. Happily, in his case, it was a near miss. The dangers of an ocean crossing are more spectacular; but those of inshore waters are no less real—and drowning is much the same anywhere.

As Uffa says, a cabin top carried out to the ship's side gave more room below and made for a stronger hull, and I have always been puzzled as to why it was not employed more often? It forced a man to crawl to get forward, and perhaps that was why it was disliked?

Sail and Power
and
Racing, Cruising and Design

A great many people have written to me expressing appreciation of my three previous books and, like Oliver Twist, have asked for more. In complying with their requests once again this year, I do not forget what I said in my Introduction to *Sail and Power* (1936), namely that I would let a year go by without publishing a book rather than, for lack of material, lower the high standard I have always tried to maintain. A glance through the pages of *Racing, Cruising and Design* will show that so far from suffering from lack of material, I have been able to include a very large number indeed of magnificent vessels of all types.

It is through the great kindness and generosity of the greatest yacht designers in the world that I have been able, once more, to produce in this book such wonderful examples of the designer's and shipwright's art. Every vessel in the book is a good type of craft for the work for which she was designed and built.

Throughout my life people have been very kind to me, and I hope that these pages, as those of my other books, are equally friendly, for then they reflect the generosity shown to me by all the people with whom I have come into contact in this world.

There are two ways of teaching: (1) The bitter way, by taking bad examples and pointing out the faults in each case, and (2) The better way, to my mind, of taking perfect examples and pointing out the perfection in the different details for people to admire and love. And this has been my way through life; and so people will look in vain for hard criticism in these pages, for I have always only asked for the best types of boats, and once more can place my hand on my heart and say I would love to own any one of the vessels in this book.

from *Introduction* to *Racing, Cruising and Design*

To Brittany in Brynhild

Owner, Uffa Fox
Designer, Uffa Fox
Builder, Uffa Fox

LOA 20 ft. 0 in.
LWL 19 ft. 6 in.
Beam 4 ft. 0 in.
Draught 4 ft. 9 in.
Displacement 650 lbs.
Sail area 130 sq. ft.

If we are fond of music, we play some instrument or sing, so that we may enjoy it; and if we are fond of the sea, we must sail on it in some form of boat. Our choice of a boat is as wide as our choice of a musical instrument; and for a cruise across channel and along the Normandy and Brittany coasts into the Bay of Biscay to Spain and possibly the Mediterranean, I chose, designed and built a 20-foot double-handed sliding-seat canoe.

I am very fortunate in being able to enjoy sailing in every kind of vessel, from a Thames Barge to a "J" class boat and from an ocean racer to a racing canoe. The choice of *Brynhild* was not a blind one, but was made for several reasons:

(1) I know nothing more exhilarating than flying low over the water at 12 to 15 knots on the end of a canoe's sliding seat.

(2) Such a boat with her speed would be a good performer even to windward.

(3) She would enable us to explore many little harbours and dart in amongst the rocks which are scattered everywhere along the Brittany and Normandy coasts, west of Cherbourg, and

(4) I am now getting on in life, and have only a few more years in which I can really enjoy sailing so small a boat, in which with the least wind one is wet through all the while. In such a boat one has all the excitement of a gale of wind in a fresh breeze, when the seas call for constant attention and demand every ounce of her helmsman's ability. Sailing her for eight hours, one puts forth as much care and attention, and understanding of wind and waves, as one would in four times that length of time in a larger vessel.

I designed *Brynhild* in the autumn of 1935. Her plan shows that she has very long and easy buttocks, and is an easily driven craft with powerful sections, and capable of a very high speed. Having, in a 17-foot sliding-seat canoe, sailed 16·3 knots over the Medina measured $\frac{1}{2}$ mile (a performance which took four months and an untold number of efforts to accomplish), I thought that a 20-footer with two up might plane at 20 knots, but we have so far only sailed at 15 knots. Generally in those half mile runs I became exhausted physically, as battling with a sliding seat canoe in a hard wind calls for perfect physical fitness,

and even then one burns up far more energy than can be afforded: hence the advantage of having two up.

As the construction plan shows, she is very lightly built. This is necessary for a cruising canoe, as it enables her to climb the seas, and also enables her crew to carry her up over a beach. In this plan will be seen the wooden drop keel, the bottom of which is ballasted by 50 lbs. of lead, and abaft this the rudder, dropping down through the trunk, so that it is quickly removable when coming into shallow water.

Over the drop keel two sliding seats are seen, and the deck plan shows the various hatch openings. The four small hatches in the watertight cockpit were never used; instead we used four other hatches in the sides of the cockpit, as these were easier to keep tight. Aft will be seen one large hatchway between the rudder and cockpit, in which we stowed a watertight box for special gear, and right aft was a very small hatch used for sponging water out of the stern when on a slipway.

Her timbers, $\frac{5}{16}$ in. $\times \frac{3}{16}$ in., are spaced $1\frac{3}{4}$ in. centres, and to these the $\frac{1}{16}$ in. bare diagonal planking is fastened. After a skin of oiled silk, the $\frac{1}{8}$ in. bare planking is fastened by 17-gauge nails, which are clenched on the insides of the timbers. The deck, of $\frac{5}{32}$ in. thick sea-resisting plywood, is fastened to $1\frac{5}{8}$ in. $\times \frac{3}{8}$ in. beams spaced 10 in. apart; the effect of this light construction is that, though 20 ft. long, the canoe weighs no more than 190 lbs., which two men can carry up a beach.

The sections show a sliding seat swung right out to one side and it is surprising how the sail carrying ability of a canoe is increased by her crew of two sitting four feet out beyond her side. These seats, when evenly slid on either side, make fine carrying planks, easily held and strong enough for us to carry *Brynhild* by them, with a man at each end lifting the bow and stern to steady her.

In the first sail plan the mainboom runs forward of the mast and takes the tack of the jib, the idea of this being that as the main sheet is eased the jib is too, for being sheeted on the boom it swings at all times with the mainsail, and besides this the forestay, pulling up on the fore end of the boom, prevents the after end cocking up when the sheet is eased, which means that the sail swings out in one plane like a door. Now, though this is a fine rig for a steady wind, we found it was no good in puffy weather, for then when we eased the sheet in a squall, the whole rig swung round and the wind spilled out everywhere at once, so that we had either all the sail drawing or none at all. For our cruise therefore we went back to the normal rig as shown by the second sail plan and photographs; with this we could ease the mainsail right away, with the jib still pulling. With a total area of 120 sq. ft., we could ease away two-thirds in the mainsail and let the remaining third in the staysail pull her through a squall, or by easing half the mainsail we could ease away one-third; and this made her sailing much easier.

Original caption : Fifteen knots was the highest speed attained
by Brynhild.

The mast for the second rig did not revolve as the first did, though like the first it was stepped on the deck.

It was early in December when we launched *Brynhild*, and a SW gale was blowing, which was full of very hard slams, such as are only experienced in the dead of winter. Thus on our very first sail we saw the disadvantage of a rig which was not elastic, and which forced us to have the sails right full or empty. We at once changed over to the other rig, intending to test the revolving rig later when the weather settled down. Actually we have never done so. Though we sailed *Brynhild* through December and the rest of the winter months we never reached a speed of 20 knots, 15 knots being the highest we ever obtained.

Thursday, June 18. At 6.00 a.m. we were under way with a light easterly wind, and the tide still against us in through the Needles. It was not until 7.30 a.m. that we passed the Needles Rocks, being able to steer SSW, close hauled, the wind being SE, the sky overcast and rain falling. Though this course was slightly to leeward of our course for Cherbourg, the wind was strong enough to let us walk along at some five knots, which was quite satisfactory.

As we got further offshore the wind continued to freshen, and the rain to get heavier, although visibility was good, being about five miles. The wind then freed, and enabled us to lay our course for Cherbourg with the wind abeam. As the wind was steadily freshening, we knew it was only a question of time before we would have to reef down and go slower because of the seas, so we drove *Brynhild* as hard as we could while we were able, and she rushed across the tops of the waves at 10 or 12 knots, every so often slowing down to about 4 knots when she stuck her bow into the sea in front. As we crossed the steamer line we judged the speed of the wind to be 25 to 30 miles an hour, for the steamers

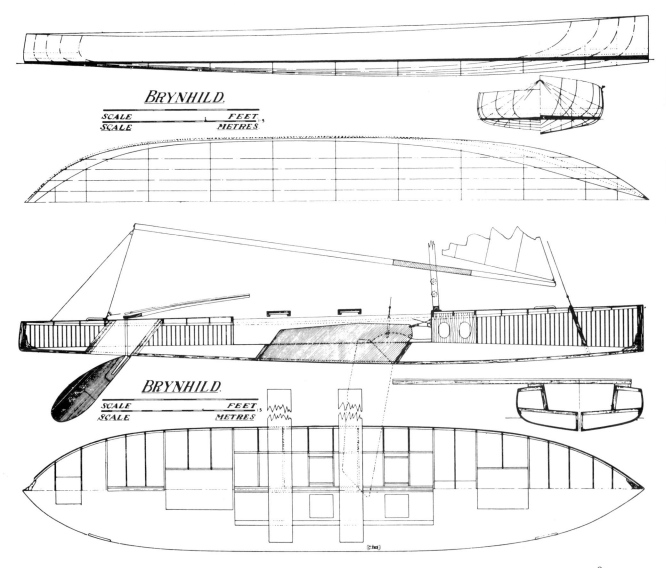

BRYNHILD.

SCALE   FEET.
SCALE   METRES.

BRYNHILD.

SCALE   FEET.
SCALE   METRES.

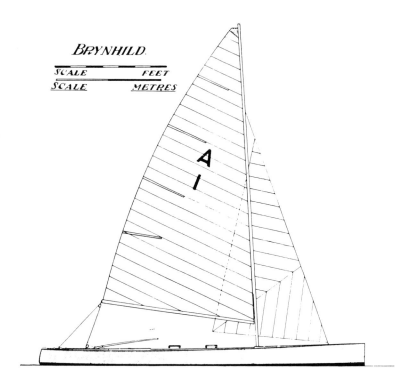

BRYNHILD.

SCALE	FEET
SCALE	METRES

were going along at 15 knots and their smoke was being blown ahead of them as fast as they were travelling. We continued pushing *Brynhild* with full sail. Steering was very tricky work, for at the speed we were travelling it seemed possible to roll her completely over by giving her a lot of helm at once, and so I had to anticipate her every move in advance, using only the smallest amount of rudder. It was most exciting rushing along in this sea, for when we got on the face of a wave, we would, it seemed, tear along at 30 miles an hour, though of course it was no more than 12 or 14. At 10.00 a.m. a very heavy squall settled it and we had to reef. First of all we took in the jib and then reefed the mainsail. We still had too much sail and were travelling too fast for the sea running, so we rolled up some more until finally the number in the top of the sail was only just showing clear above the boom, and even with this tiny amount of sail, some 20 sq. ft., we were going 7 and 8 knots, too fast for the sea running, but because of her light displacement *Brynhild* did not disturb the sea at all, and so all was well.

Some time after this the wind eased, so we gave her the jib; this was too much, so it came in again, and we unrolled some of the mainsail, being able to adjust our sail area to suit the seas in this way. Throughout the day we reefed and unreefed, as an easterly wind is never true in strength of direction. Finally the wind dropped so that we could carry full sail. As we were approaching the French coast our speed eased down to some 4 knots. At 2.35 p.m. the land behind Cherbourg was in

sight about 9 or 10 miles away, but we had hardly a breath of wind, and the land became blotted out by fog. At 3.15 p.m. we were becalmed, and it was not until 7.30 p.m. that we entered Cherbourg with a very faint air from the ESE, exactly 12 hours from the Needles, our average across being only 5 knots. Up to the time of sighting the French coast through the fog, we had averaged 7 knots, and had the wind not increased and blown so hard we might easily have averaged 10. Even so, it was quite a fast passage for such a small boat.

Among the items carried were two Primus stoves and a typewriter. This brings forth, in our imagination, an entrancing picture of Uffa hanging on by one toe while cooking eggs and bacon with one hand and typing out an article with the other. It was not quite like that; but there *is* an authentic photo of his crew, Bill, cooking at sea, between the squalls, off Chausey.

The French call this "le Côte Sauvage", the savage coast, and what with the racing tides, the rocks, and the fog, they may well be right. *Brynhild* encountered all these things. She was within a hand's reach of the rocks in places, and they sailed her through thick fog. They came to a close rapport with the Breton folk, which might not have been possible with a bigger boat. There were still primitive scenes to be observed then. They watched fishermen on a rope-walk twist up 30 fathoms of two-strand rope, made out of reeds, in 15 minutes. In the smaller places half the village came down to carry *Brynhild* up above the high-tide mark. They camped on lonely shores, and sometimes dined in big hotels, they fought for their lives amid rocks which would have smashed their canoe instantly, and at the end of the cruise *Brynhild* was laid up in the cellar of the Hotel des Baines at Pontusval surrounded by wines and champagne.

Uffa on the seat of Brynhild.

Roland von Bremen

Owner, Kaufmannschaft der Hansestadt
Designer, Henry Gruber
Builder, Yachtwerft Burmester

LOA 59 ft. 0 in.
LWL 42 ft. 8 in.
Beam 13 ft. 5 in.
Draught 8 ft. 3 in.
Displacement 25·6 tons
Sail area 1,442 sq. ft.

The *Roland von Bremen* was designed for this year's Transatlantic Race from Bermuda to Cuxhaven, and her designer, knowing that almost all the course would be running and reaching, gave her a rather full fore body with fine lines aft. This, instead of harming her sea-going ability, would probably tend to improve it, for a vessel with a fine clean run does not disturb the following sea so much, so can be driven harder when chasing away before the wind and carry on longer than one which has full quarters.

There is no doubt that *Roland von Bremen*'s lines did prove most successful, for she won the race quite easily.

To drive this fast set of lines Henry gave *Roland* a very efficient Bermudian rig, so popular owing to the rules governing ocean racers to-day. The value of the mizen itself is questionable, but the rig pays because of the mizen staysails, which are free, and are very fine sails when the least bit off the wind.

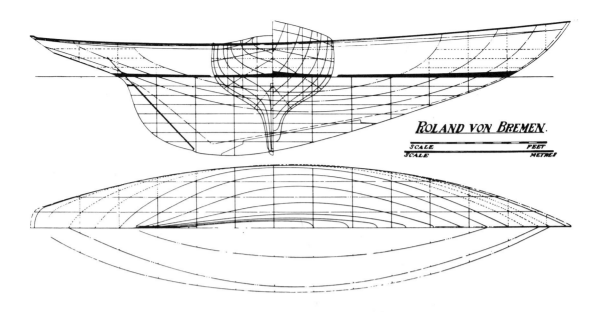

Roland von Bremen.

The mainmast, 66 ft. above the deck, is 20 ft. from the stem-head, and the clearance between the luffs of the two headsails is over 5 ft., which enables the headsails to be worked easily.

To race over a course such as this transatlantic one of 3,600 miles, an ocean racer must be easily handled and well behaved, otherwise she would wear her crew out, for an ocean racer is driven far harder than a cruiser,

Roland von Bremen

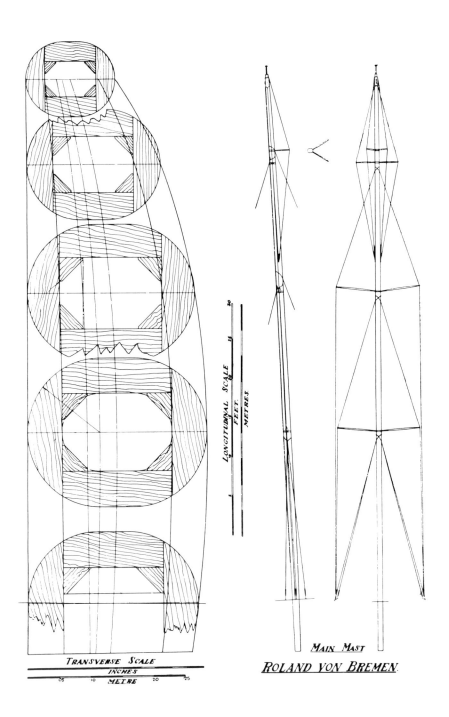

TRANSVERSE SCALE
INCHES
05   10   METRE   20   25

LONGITUDINAL SCALE
FEET.
METRES

MAIN MAST
ROLAND VON BREMEN.

who tucks her head under her wing, while the ocean racer has to carry on in order to stand a chance of winning; and it is because of this that ocean racers have so improved the design of cruising vessels.

The construction plan shows a good stiff girder to take the thrust of the mainmast, and looking over this plan we see that every part has been designed and developed to withstand the strains and stresses that it is

called upon to endure, for Henry Gruber, having assisted Burgess in the design of so many fast vessels, such as *Enterprise*, *Rainbow*, *Niña*, etc., has an intimate and vast knowledge of the strains and stresses put upon the various members of a sailing vessel when raced hard. *Roland von Bremen* was only able to use her mainsail five days on the way across the Atlantic, most of the passage being made under a trysail and a reefed

89

spinnaker, so we see it was a hard drive across, which only a seaworthy and well built vessel could have endured.

In another part of the volume containing plans of *Roland von Bremen* is reproduced Sherman Hoyt's personal diary when he accompanied the Germans on the Transatlantic Race. They were intent on steering a Great Circle compass course and wily old Sherman, with forty years experience, only wanted to give the ship an easy motion and keep the sails asleep and have her pointing in roughly the right direction. He thought the Germans were "compass card crazy".

However, in his preamble to the diary Sherman admits that, written in the heat of the moment, it conveys an impression of acerbity greater than really existed. The language difficulty did not help either. At the end of the voyage they were all good shipmates. Even during it Sherman, in his diary, praises their seamanship and their guts. He also finds the Teutonic thoroughness of the spares carried, and their careful stowage, refreshing after some American yachts of his acquaintance. The more surprising therefore is the lack of an emergency tiller when the collar on the rudder stock for the wheel steering kept slipping.

Spica

Owner, J. T. Hunt
Designer, H. W. de Voogt
Builder, Haarlem Yacht Building Co.

LOA 50 ft. 0 in.
LWL 34 ft. 0 in.
Beam 11 ft. 6 in.
Draught 6 ft. 6 in.
Displacement 12·6 tons
Sail area 1,300 sq. ft.

Every yacht we become acquainted with appears to have a character of its own, and it seems to me that yachts, like dogs and other animals, develop their characters from their owners. Boats that under one owner have been hard weather boats only, turn out to be light weather cracks when owned by another man, and sometimes a bad-tempered dog will turn out quite amiable under new ownershjip.

Spica has always struck me as a happy little vessel, full of contentment, and yet one that is still restless enough to win races; for if we are too contented in this world we have no power or dash, so our serenity must be tempered with a certain amount of driving force. It is difficult to say just who supplies this force aboard *Spica*, but I strongly suspect her owner, J. T. Hunt, as underneath his smile and chuckle one feels a great deal of energy stored up.

In 1930 it blew very hard for the Royal Ocean Racing Club's channel race, and every yacht in the race gave up on account of the weather except *Spica*. Those of us who have experienced an August gale realise the hardihood and endurance displayed by *Spica* and those aboard on this occasion. This alone would recommend *Spica* to us, but she is the heroine of many such races and cruises, and when we look at her lines we realise that she is a sturdy little cruiser.

She is a full bodied boat, as one would expect from the accommodation one finds when going below, her sections being particularly good for this type of vessel, while her water-lines and buttocks are easy and fair, as are the diagonals. The stern post, being some 3 feet forward of the after end of the water-line, cuts down the wetted surface without causing her to be wild on the helm, for, as will be seen from the profile, she has a long keel, and generally speaking, she is a good type of vessel, beamy, with moderate draught, and a fairly long keel, and yet quite fast and able.

Spica's accommodation is exceptional for so small a vessel. She has a double-berthed fo'c'sle forward of the mast, with a galley in it at the after end, and immediately abaft this is her main saloon, the backs of the settee forming upper berths when cruising with a crowd aboard, and in this little saloon many happy evenings have been spent by those aboard, the night being filled with music and song. I imagine *Spica*'s owner has introduced more youngsters into the mysteries of ocean racing than any other man, and *Spica*'s crew is mostly recruited from Oxford and Cambridge, some, in spite of their youth, having sailed thousands of miles, and all of them happy and full of song when aboard *Spica*. Abaft this will be seen the double or ladies' cabin, with a washroom between it and the saloon, and from this the companion way over the bridge deck leads into the watertight cockpit under which is situated *Spica*'s engine, while the hatch

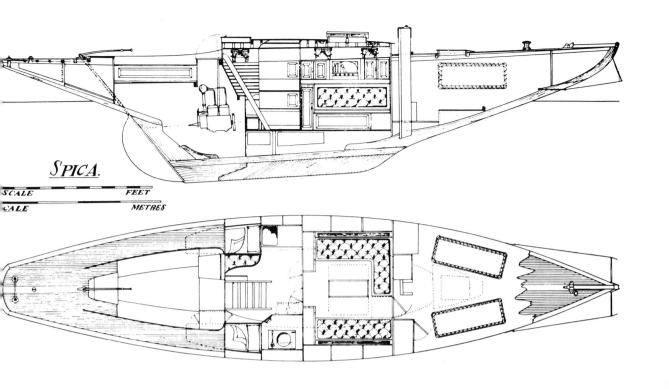

SPICA.

SCALE   FEET

CALE   METRES

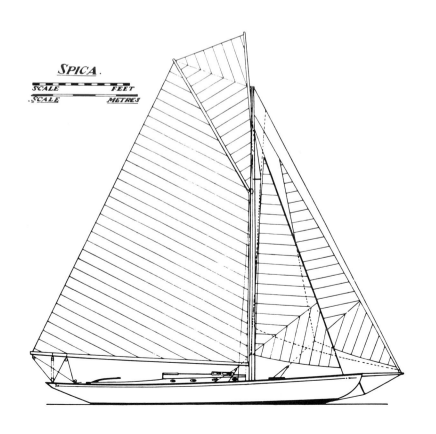

SPICA.

SCALE   FEET

SCALE   METRES

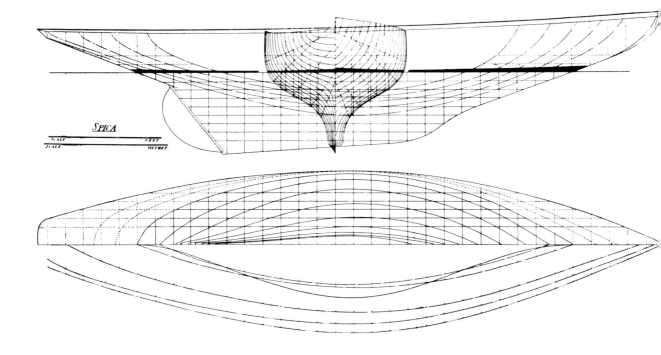

SPICA.

SCALE   FEET
SCALE   METRES

under the tiller opens into the sail locker. There is no doubt *Spica* with her combination of comfort, seaworthiness and speed is a type of cruiser that will appeal to many.

The sail plan shows her high-peaked gaff rig with a topsail set above, and while this rig looks old-fashioned and slow, *Spica* has never had any trouble with her mast and spars though she has split and carried away many sails in her time, for sails get tired and worn when called upon to endure as much as *Spica*'s are.

Built in Holland in 1915, *Spica* has a tabernacle mast for bridges, and though she has cruised down to Spain and across the Bay of Biscay she has never experienced any trouble or difficulty with her mast stepped this way. It might even seem to be an advantage, for if the mast is held firmly at the step and in the deck, and is allowed to bend over to leeward as most are, it is subjected to strains which *Spica*'s mast is free from. Built as long as twenty years ago, *Spica* still has a great deal to recommend her to us, for after all, though twenty years seems a long time to us it is very little when we consider that the wind and waves have remained the same since the beginning of time, so if a vessel is suited to the sea in any one age, she must suit it for all time.

Spica has won the Channel Race, 1930, 1932, 1933 and has won the Forsyth Cup for the first yacht home in the Channel Race every year from 1930 to 1935 with the exception of 1931. This year, 1936, she won the Royal Ocean Racing Club's event from Falmouth to the Clyde, all of which will give an idea of *Spica* and her owner's ability at sea.

Spica's run of successes show that a gaff-rigged yacht could still be competitive in the early Thirties. Looking at that sail plan I am struck by the area of sail she carried. I also have an awful vision of that long gaff flailing around aloft, and of a man standing on the last few inches of counter to reach the boom end—but perhaps it was not as bad as all that. Uffa comments on her mast, stepped in a tabernacle, and that they "never experienced any trouble or difficulty"; but in a later era of yachting deck-stepped masts became very common, and the stresses on the mast are virtually the same.

Note, on the accommodation profile drawing, the little curtains, the cabin book-shelf, with its rail to keep the books in place, and the panelling—all faithfully drawn in. I must say I loathe curtains on a boat, and had always thought of them as a modern innovation; but apparently they have always been with us.

92

Vailima II

Owner, Walter Bergius
Designers, Walter Bergius and Sydney Graham
Builder, James A. Silver, Ltd.

LOA 78 ft. 0 in.
LWL 68 ft. 6 in.
Beam 16 ft. 0 in.
Draught 6 ft. 6 in.
Displacement 45 tons
Sail area 1,685 sq. ft.
Engine, Kelvin Diesel 66 horse power
Diameter of propeller 30 in.
Pitch of propeller 21 in.
Speed of propeller 750 revs. per min.
Speed over measured mile 9 knots
Miles per gallon 3

Vailima II is one of the most successful vessels designed, and this is not to be wondered at when we consider that her owner, an ardent lover of sail, is also the maker of marine engines, with some forty years of active experience in sail and power from which to draw inspiration.

In this country vessels that are meant to sail as well as run under power are called fifty-fifty vessels, meaning that they are cross breeds with a 50 per cent. ability under power and a 50 per cent. sailing ability. Generally speaking, however, they are such poor performers under canvas that their sails are of little use except for steadying them in a seaway.

But in *Vailima II* we see something far better than a fifty-fifty. She is a full powered vessel, and she is also a good enough performer under sail to win races. As a power vessel, she has yet to meet the wind and sea to slow her down below her steering speed; it is the

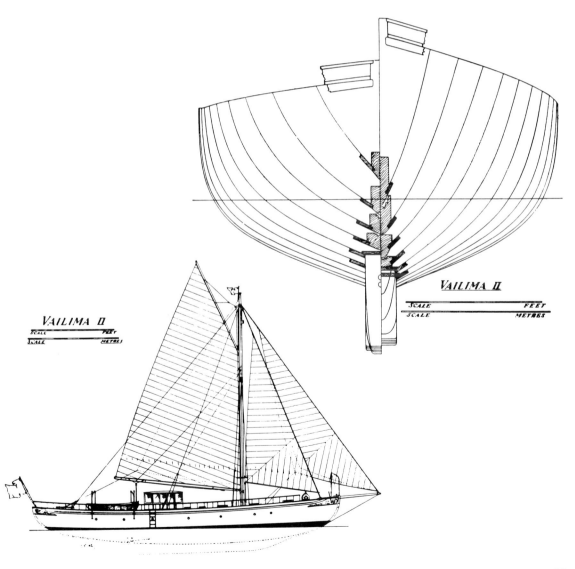

VAILIMA II

SCALE   FEET
SCALE   METRES

VAILIMA II

SCALE   FEET
SCALE   METRES

93

engine that has always had to be slowed down, since it is powerful enough to drive her into a head sea so that she ships water by the ton unless speed is reduced. Under canvas, in six starts in the Hunter's Quay to Tarbert race she has won two first prizes, one in a strong reaching wind and the other involving a dead beat of fifteen miles with a great number of tacks. And with a heavy wind abeam and her trysail and storm headsails set she has sailed fifty miles in five hours.

and make such little leeway when beating. In a word, *Vailima II* is successful because she started life by being well thought out, and to-day, after six years, her owner would make only minor alterations if he were to design another ship to take her place.

The sail plan shows a gaff cutter rig, the two headsails meeting at the top of the mast fifty feet above the deck, while the gaff goes higher and raises the peak of the mainsail sixty feet above deck. So well balanced

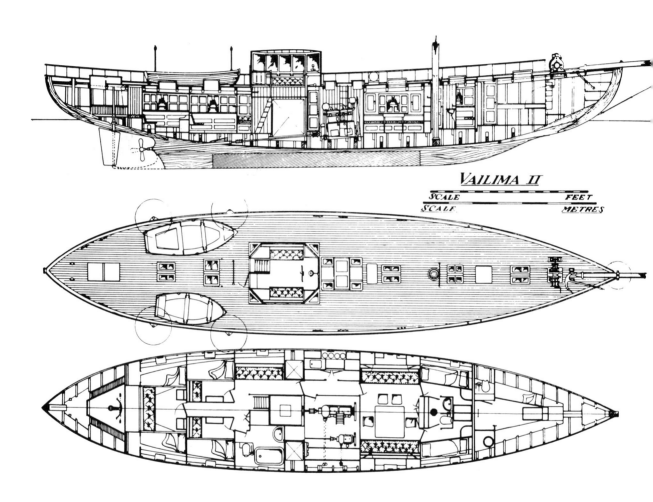

VAILIMA II

The lines show us an easily driven hull, with a midship section approximating to a half-circle, the value of which I have emphasized in a previous chapter. *Vailima*'s lines reveal great understanding on the part of her owner; studying them, we cease to wonder at her unique performance of 9 knots with 66 h.p., for this easily driven hull is driven exactly to her wave-making speed, and for such a speed it would be almost impossible to improve upon her lines.

The deep false keel or deadwood running along plumb for some three quarters of her underwater length explains why she is able to hold up to weather

is this rig that a reefed mainsail calls for a smaller jib and the lowering of the staysail makes her hard on the helm. The boats stow aft, and for this reason no mizen was fitted, as its rigging would interfere with their swinging inboard. Now though in the plan *Vailima* looks a little naked aft without any sail, she does not give this impression when under way. I have seen her sailing both in Scottish and south coast waters, and always found her an exceptionally good-looking ship, delightfully easy on the eye. No doubt this is partly accounted for by her unexpected ability under sail, for most things that are able are good to look at. Neither a

Thames barge nor a windmill were designed for looks; everything about them has a purpose, and because of this, not in spite of it, both are a pleasure to watch, and so it is with *Vailima II*.

With all her virtues *Vailima II* must have some faults. The only two I can suggest are both very minor ones, the first being that, to my mind, the deadwood or false keel could have run a little farther aft on its lower edge, and this should have carried a band or skeg to the rudder heel, so forming a support for the bottom of the rudder. In the case of her running over a warp this skeg would prevent it fouling the propeller or the rudder; and though it is true that she has twice grounded on rocks without damage to her rudder or propeller, the skeg would offer protection to these in such circumstances. A disadvantage to her section is that it is impossible to have a deep sump for the bilge suction, and a very little aboard her runs high upon her sides in a seaway, and so has to be chased with the suction hose.

While, as would be supposed, she will stay with certainty in a good breeze, great care has to be exercised in beating up a narrow channel. Generally, however, *Vailima* comes to anchor in an intricate harbour under power.

Vailima II, then, is a very fine example of the combination of sail and power, and her owner is to be congratulated on having the understanding to evolve such a notable vessel.

Since most yawls and ketches seem to go to windward just as well without the mizen, perhaps this vessel is not quite as daft as she looks? A motor/sailer is the supreme test for a yacht-designer. Certainly, a motor boat with sails hung on her is a useless object. Sailing gear is not cheap and many of the owners of such craft would be better off with a good twin-screw motor cruiser which made no pretensions of being anything else. Mention of folding propellers here shows that they are by no means a recent development. Uffa's simile, "fold aft like a duck's foot" is very apt, for that is exactly what they do. Nature has usually preceded man's ideas.

Bonnie Dundee

Owner, Clifford Mallory
Designer, Luders Marine Construction Co.
Builder, Luders Marine Construction Co.

LOA 66 ft. 9 in.
LWL 56 ft. 6 in.
Beam 16 ft. 0 in.
Draught 5 ft. 0 in.
Displacement 33 tons
Sail area 1,300 sq. ft.
Speed 10½ knots
2 Engines 4″ bore by 5½″ stroke 60 h.p. each Buda
   Diesel. 1,500 revs.
Diameter of Propeller 32 in.
Pitch of Propeller 29 in.

Bonnie Dundee is the result of the many years of experience of her owner Clifford Mallory, one of America's leading yachtsmen. She has given an excellent account of herself in calm and in gale, and has proved a first class ship in action; and when a man of Clifford Mallory's wide experience is pleased with a vessel, we can be sure she is good.

Forty years ago he owned his first boat larger than a dinghy, and since then has sailed every kind of vessel imaginable. His last three boats were of similar type and were all named *Bonnie Dundee*, the first being a 37-foot ketch-rigged lifeboat type of boat with a 24 horse power engine, the second the 48-foot *Bonnie Dundee* with a 60–80 Buda Diesel giving a speed of just over 9 knots. This third boat, as one would expect, is larger still, being 66 ft. 9 ins. overall with a total horse power of 120. After having sailed over 10,000 miles in the

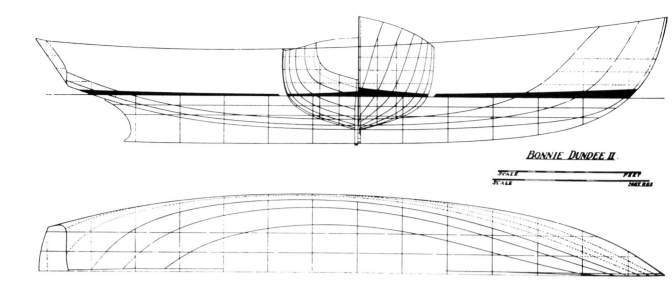

BONNIE DUNDEE II

SCALE _____ FEET
SCALE _____ METRES

present *Bonnie Dundee* in the first year of her life, her owner is well satisfied and thinks that her general proportion of sail, power, etc., would be found most suitable for both larger and smaller vessels, and that a yacht 90 to 100 feet long of this type would make the finest world cruising vessel imaginable.

Clifford Mallory, having decided to build his latest vessel, chose well when he took his ideas to the Luders Marine Construction Co., for they were sympathetic and put their own knowledge into the new *Bonnie Dundee*. They, too, for a long time had felt that the so-called motor sailer was neither fish, flesh, fowl, nor good red herring as she was generally underpowered, and the sails did little more than steady her in a seaway. A great many people might not believe that *Bonnie Dundee* would go to windward and come about without the aid of her engines, but a study of her lines reveals the fact that she is very sweet and easy under water; she has a fine and easy entrance and quite a clean run, while the long flat keel gives her a good grip to windward, so there is nothing under water to stop her from sailing. Such a shape is ideal for a power vessel of normal speed, and one can imagine her riding out any sea in even a winter's gale without coming to much harm, for she is a lively and buoyant vessel similar to our national lifeboats which are of course generally used only in the worst of winter weather, the conditions yachtsmen try, if possible, to avoid. We know that our lifeboats sail quite well, and remembering this we are able to appreciate the weatherly and seaworthy qualities of *Bonnie Dundee*.

The sail plan shows an easily worked ketch rig. In tacking no sheet need be touched, only the back stays from the mizen being eased away and set up on the new weather side. Such a rig makes for certainty in stays, for if the wind and sea made it doubtful as to her coming

round, the mizen could be hauled to weather as she was shot into the wind, with a staysail lashed to the old lee shrouds, the mizen to weather would spring her head to the wind and with the staysail would pay her head off and she would be about. This is the way our barges are tacked in narrow channels; time after time they have to stay before they have gathered full way, and sometimes the mate, as the helm is put down, lowers the staysail and runs it up immediately after, the mizen in the meantime having sprung the barge head to wind, the staysail being hoisted up puts her head off on the new tack. It would be only on very rare occasions, such as beating in narrow waters, that such measures would be needed with *Bonnie Dundee*, for with her 1,300 sq. ft. of sail she is exceptionally handy, her tall rig being made possible and practicable by the use of hollow spars and stainless steel, for her iron keel weighs only three tons. Iron was chosen as the boat has been used for sailing in the Bahamas, where in exploring the shallow waters she frequently touched the coral bottom where if she had had a lead keel she would have stuck fast and damaged it, whereas with an iron one it was a simple matter to back her off. In this respect again she resembles our national lifeboats, which have found an iron keel to be best for their work.

To avoid galvanic action all the fastenings in the hull proper were specially made of hot dipped galvanized iron or steel, the deck fittings, fenders, etc., being of stainless steel as far as possible to avoid labour, and where this could not be used they are of bronze, chromium plated.

Bonnie Dundee is planked with Oregon pine on closely spaced frames and has four watertight bulkheads, the deck and cabin top being of teak.

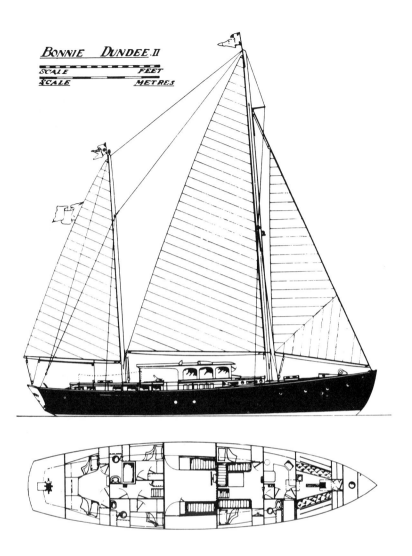

Bonnie Dundee·II

I cannot agree with Uffa when he says, "..., and from this it can be seen that the deck house extends to the mizen, and so forms a fine platform on which to reef and handle the main sail". I have never cruised in a big motor/sailer; but several times I had a day out aboard one newly built. This was when I worked as a yachting journalist and·the final trials were combined with a "Press Day" in the hope of some good "write-ups" in the yachting magazines. It always seemed to me that men working on the top of a deck house stowing the mainsail were in danger of being thrown off by an extra heavy roll, and they would have pitched clean over the side deck into the "drink".

On these trips we hoisted all the sails so that the new yacht could be photographed "under sail" — something to go in the magazines. On the way back into the Hamble River, hands from the yard which built her would be busily stowing the sails neatly and putting the covers back on. Cynical journalists would mutter, in an aside, "That's the last time they'll ever be used." Was this an unmitigated slander? Properly designed, a motor/sailer may be quite successful; but mountainous deck-houses must detract from sailing performance.

Vema III

Owner, George Unger Vetlesen
Designer, Johan Anker
Builder, Anker & Jensen

LOA 70 ft. 0 in.
LWL 45 ft. 6 in.
Beam 11 ft. 10 in.
Draught 9 ft. 0 in.
Displacement 27½ tons,
Sail area 2,080 sq. ft.

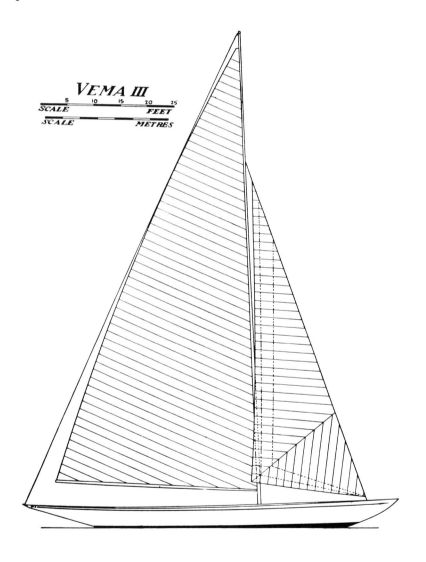

Such a boat as *Vema III* proves that the present international rule has succeeded in developing a cruiser for racing purposes, or, put the other way round, a racer that is a fine cruiser. This rule, with certain alterations, is now some thirty years old, so should be near perfection, though we all at times criticise parts of it, it being man's nature to look critically at the things he loves best.

The principle of the international rule is ably expressed by Johan Anker. It is an expression in measurement of the speed factors, being a balance between driving power (sail area) and the length

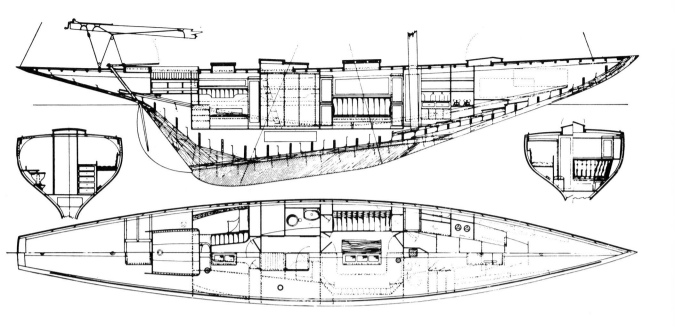

(speed) a boat uses when sailing, and not the length she floats at when at anchor. In some of the hottest international classes we see boats of varying length, sail area and beam; and looking at such a collection one would say, "If that one is fast that one must be slow," and yet these boats will race and at the end of a 20 or 40 mile course only seconds separate them. Thus it would seem that the international rule is successful in spite of (or possibly because of) our criticism, for true criticism, provided it is constructive, is bound to improve the thing criticised.

Vema's stemline runs perfectly straight, from just above the water for a length of some 23 ft. where it meets the keel line, which is also straight for a distance of 14 ft., such a line being a joy to those making up her cradle for hauling out. This arrangement does not interfere with her lines at all, for they are easy and fair throughout, there being no distortion whatever in any single line, for all blend together in perfect harmony, and in *Vema III* Johan Anker has produced a very fine model of a vessel.

The accommodation and construction plans show the pipe cots in the fo'c'sle for *Vema*'s crew, immediately abaft of which is a galley and pantry. Aft of this is her main cabin or saloon, the table being immediately under the skylight and therefore well lit.

To starboard the U-shaped settee looks very comfortable, this being dotted in, as the starboard half shows the deck plan, the port half being the accommodation. The door in the after end of the saloon leads on to a passage, to port of which is a wash room, while just aft of the centre line is the main companion way and to starboard a single-berthed cabin, while farther aft is the double-berthed cabin. The watertight cockpit cutting into this at the centre does not interfere with

two sleeping berths, as the floor of the cockpit is some 4 ft. above that of the cabin, there being 2 ft. 6 in. space between the bunk and this floor. The counter is given over as a sail locker.

The sail plan shows that her mainmast is stepped 26 ft. abaft her stem, and, as one would expect, the sail height chosen is the limit allowed by the rule, 25 metres above the deck, for the international rule allows masts to be twice the rating in metres plus 1 metre. In a 12-metre's case this is 25 metres, which is 82 ft. 6 in., such a rig enabling the "12's" to carry a permanent backstay to the end of the counter, so that in tacking there is only the backstay or runner pulling aft from the hounds, which takes the pull of the forestay to be worked. Though these 12-metres are so easily handled, it is surprising how much energy they demand in a keen race in hard weather. After such a race of 40 miles, I have come ashore feeling every bit as tired as I used to after a hard football match, for the vessels are driven to their utmost when racing in order to win, and it is not so much the weight of the canvas as the weight of the wind in it. Even with six of us aboard besides the helmsman, the jib sheets demand the utmost strength at just the right moment when short tacking, and only those who have crewed aboard all racers from "J" boats down to canoes realise the physical as well as mental energy these boats demand when raced to the utmost. I have seen many races lost through crews and helmsmen tiring for the last part of the race.

The thunder of a "J" boat's canvas as she tacks in a hard wind makes us realise the power and weight in her sails, and the sight of two men sitting well out to weather of a 14-footer in a breeze enables us to realise the physical strength required in these boats. "Twelves", "Eights" and "Sixes" in between may not create

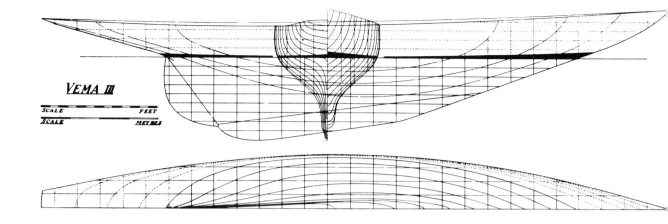

VEMA III

SCALE   FEET

SCALE   METRES

such a vivid picture, but nevertheless they claim all the vigour both of mind and body a man can give them, and every class has its attractions, just as every age has its charm.

Vema's sail plan only shows three headsails, but she of course has genoas, and intermediates to suite every kind of wind. Designed and built three years ago by Johan Anker for G. Unger Vetlesen, *Vema* has raced with a fair amount of success in Norwegian and European waters, and while in British waters won a reputation for her light weather ability. Even now, some years after her visit, 12-metre people still have vivid recollections of this, while her long water-line length enables her to travel fast in a breeze. In *Vema*, then, we have a racer fast in light or hard weather that is also a comfortable cruiser, a type of vessel those responsible for the international rule should be proud of, for when designers such as Anker, who understand the rule and all its ways, produce such a vessel to race and when she wins races in the largest class on the international rule (for above this size the universal rule governs the design), there can evidently be very little indeed wrong with it.

In view of what has happened to the "Twelves" when since adopted for the America's Cup, it is amusing to hear Uffa, in his opening sentence, refer to: ". . . a cruiser for racing purposes, or, put the other way round, a racer that is a fine cruiser." There may be other America's Cup matches sailed in "Twelves" and perhaps it would be salutary to consider the manner in which these boats were first conceived. Note the orthodox accommodation on *Vema III*—a fo'c'sle for the paid hands with pantry and galley adjoining (a cook-steward would probably be carried), a fine big saloon, washroom, main companionway and single cabin, then a double cabin aft. The tiller steering is interesting, too, on a 70 ft. yacht. While the mighty "J"'s still dominated the racing scene, the "Twelves" were down among the small fry. Writing in 1936, Uffa says, the Twelves sailed around the East, South and South-West coasts of England from one regatta to the next, and after racing for three hours or more, four boats would often round a mark within four seconds of each other. It is astounding that they had a crew of only six. "*Even* with six" says Uffa, he found it tiring. Why on earth did they not have a proper complement on board? *Evaine* which Uffa admired was subsequently used for America's Cup tuning by a British syndicate. She is now a cruiser and has crossed the Atlantic twice.

8 METRE
Germania II

Owner, Dr. Krupp
Designers, Abeking & Rasmussen
Builders, Abeking & Rasmussen

LOA 49 ft. 0 in.
LWL 30 ft. 6 in.
Beam 8 ft. 3 in.
Draught 6 ft. 6 in.
Displacement 10·08 tons
Sail area 833 sq. ft.

There is no doubt the 8-metres are delightful boats to race and handle, and their accommodation is such that a man can live comfortably aboard, a fact impressed upon me when sailing with Colonel Cleaver on his 8-metre, for he lives aboard all summer, racing her, however, in the handicap and not the 8-metre class.

The lines of *Germania* show that once more the lead keel is kept as low as possible, for the rule measuring the girth amidships has been altered slightly since *Conewago* was designed. *Conewago*, it will be noticed, runs in practically a straight line from the fore end of the water-line to the rudder heel; but here we see that *Germania*'s lead keel runs level for 10 ft., all of which shows that whenever we study plans of racers, we must remember the rules to which they are designed and built, and that the designer's aim is always to design the fastest boat possible within the rule, for a racer that is not fast is not a success. All of us designers love

producing successful boats, and possibly it pleases an owner to win races too.

The buttocks are easy and fair; no notice can be taken of the middle third of the inside buttock, as where this bulges down it cuts the lead keel (which is streamlined) at such a fine angle as to be of little importance here, the water-lines being the important ones at this point.

The sections are V'd forward and aft, and looking at them we realise how good the rule must be which produces such a well-formed vessel, for there is nothing but what is desirable in *Germania*'s sections, and so it is with the rest of her lines, they are those of a fast weatherly and seaworthy vessel. Without question the IYRU rule is doing good work by producing well formed and normal ships. On the whole *Germania*'s lines are those of a normal vessel, such as a designer would produce if he were asked to build a fast cruiser 30 ft 6 in. on the water-line, that would be seaworthy as well as fast and not to any rule at all.

The construction plan, which also shows the accommodation, is in keeping with her lines, and reminds us that, being built under Lloyds survey, the metre classes have to be strong and sturdy vessels.

Germania has a pipe berth in the fo'c'sle and two berths in the saloon, the washroom being on the centre line just abaft the mast. Abaft the saloon with its coach roof is a 5 ft. 6 in. cockpit for the crew to work in, the helmsman's cockpit being separated from this by a bridge deck 2 ft. wide.

The mast step, 9 ft. in length, picks up no less than ten floors and some fifteen frames, and so distributes the thrust from the mast over a great portion of the

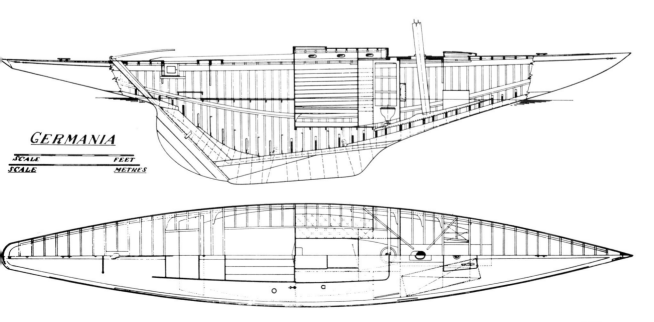

GERMANIA
SCALE ___ FEET
SCALE ___ METRES

hull, almost a third of the water-line length. The thrust of a mast is considerable, and designers have to keep this in mind when dealing with the construction plans of a vessel. *Germania*'s designers have considered every strain she will be called upon to endure.

The twelve keel bolts come through the wood keel clear of the floors, so that the keel can be taken off without disturbing the framework of the vessel, as built up and the 8 mm. lining over the frames throughout the cabin above the settee.

The coach roof gives full head room for normal people, as afloat we are generally in rubber shoes, with no heels, which in the case of a man saves an inch of headroom, while ladies without heels on their shoes often come down some three inches in height.

As would be expected the mainsail goes to the full

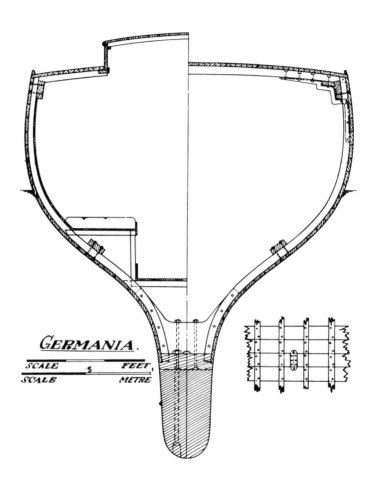

GERMANIA.

SCALE ·5 FEET

SCALE METRE

Germania's hull is built strongly and is tied together with bolts irrespective of the keel bolts. This method of bolting is good from another and equally important point of view, that of corrosion. The keel bolts must be of a metal, such as bronze or copper, and if these went through the steel floors they would set up corrosion, but being between these they are not in contact with and so less liable to eat away the steel floors, all of which is borne out by the scantling of the midship section. This on the starboard hand shows the flush deck and beam across the centre line, and we see that here the bolts in the hanging knees are through the beam only and not through the deck as well, while opposite the section at the cabin shows the coach roof

height allowed by the rule, while the height of the forestay, 12·75 metres above the deck, is also to the limit, as the rule allows the mainsail to be twice the rating (8 metres) plus 1 metre, and the fore triangle to be 75 per cent. of this, and 12.75 metres is 75 per cent. of the 17 metres.

Where we are now fitting parrot perches or a pair of jumper struts, it will be seen that *Germania* has a topmast stay to the deck, with a strut from the mast at the jib halyard height thrusting it 1 ft. 3 in. forward of the straight line. This stay, besides holding the topmast head forward, is therefore thrusting back and helping the backstay hold the luff of the jib taut. It will be noticed that this stay leads through the deck so that it

GERMANIA.

SCALE   5   10   15.   FEET

SCALE   METRES

can be eased away when the spinnaker is set.

If we look these plans over thoughtfully and carefully, we realise that in *Germania*, Abeking and Rasmussen have designed and built a fast and seaworthy racer as well as a comfortable cruiser, and her success in racing brings home the fact that if such desirable vessels can be built to the IYRU rules and win races there is very little indeed wrong with the rules.

World War 2 finished the Eight metre class, though it was dying in the late thirties. What ensured the burial of all the "metre" classes was the use of offshore racers for inshore racing. This was because boats became developed to the offshore rules such as those of the CCA and RORC, which made them enjoyable to sail on regatta courses. Remember that the "Eights"

were created by the IYRU rule of 1907. Uffa rightly says that the designer of *Germania* tried to make the boat as fast as possible under the rule. But then he gets very subjective by talking of a "well formed and normal" ship! The height of the mast, the height of the foretriangle, the narrow beam, the low freeboard, the scantlings—all are a result of the rule and to get the best possible boat for a rating of eight metres. One still wonders why if the designer was trying to save weight in the ends by placing the WC amidships aft of the mast (because the rule insisted on one), he allowed such long ends which merely added weight for no benefit. The counter admittedly took the back-stay.

For a time the "Rentokil" Eights raced on the Clyde in the sixties. "Rentokil" is the brand name of a British system for the prevention of dry and wet rot in the wood structure of buildings.

Helgoland

Designer, Henry Gruber

LOA 59 ft. 4 in. 18·084 m.
LWL 42 ft. 7¾ in. 13·00 m.
Beam 13 ft. 5 in. 4·089 m.
Draught 8 ft. 6 in. 2·590 m.
Displacement 26·5 tons 26,924 kilos.
Sail area 1,480 sq. ft. 137·60 sq. m.

Every book of mine so far has had a design in it by Henry Gruber, and because Henry combines a great mathematical brain with his artistic ability, I hope that he will always be kind enough to let me include his best plans in my books throughout the years to come, for besides being plans of fast weatherly hulls they are a great joy to look upon and study. This is not surprising when we think that Henry has helped to design successful defenders for the America's Cup, and many successful ocean racers, as well as good wholesome cruisers. Germany is indeed fortunate in having such a man within her borders, for after designing a great many years in America Henry has returned once more to his native land. The lines of *Helgoland* show a wonderful combination of speed, seaworthiness and comfort, for, though designed as a cruiser she is of the fast type encouraged by the ocean and long distance races, which are growing in popularity year by year. For a vessel to win these long races she must be seaworthy as well as fast, and also fairly comfortable to live on board, otherwise her crew are unable to drive her at all times. The comfort of the crew is very

important, for generally in small vessels such as this it is the human element which gives out first, and as the strength of a chain is in its weakest link, the human element must be studied all the while. It is for this reason that many years ago I said that the best ocean racer is the best cruiser, for while we might drive a fast uncomfortable hull round a short 200 mile course, once the distance gets over a thousand miles, comfort on board with the ability to carry food and water becomes of primary importance. When speaking of ocean races, I do not mean the short races such as our Channel race of 200 miles, which is often spoken of as an ocean race, though it does not take the vessels off soundings at all.

The construction plan shows that in *Helgoland* we have a composite hull, the frames being steel angles and the planking of wood, and as is usual with such a construction the floors and mast step are also of steel. In *Helgoland* there should be no fear of leaking at the mast step, for it will be seen that this is a substantial girder some 9 feet in length, and immediately above the step will be seen strong steel plates of the same length giving the same girder effect to the topsides, as most vessels tend to strain and lift their topsides at the mast where the pull of the shrouds is very heavy.

Another point of interest is that the forestay runs through the deck to the stem just above the water-line, thus taking all the strain off the deck; while aft we see that the mizen step is utilized as a bearing for the steering wheel spindle, and the bevelled gearing, working on the quadrant, is the stronger and better for this bearing at the mast step.

In the deck plan we see a diagonal steel strap at the forestay, two diagonals on the mainmast, and between

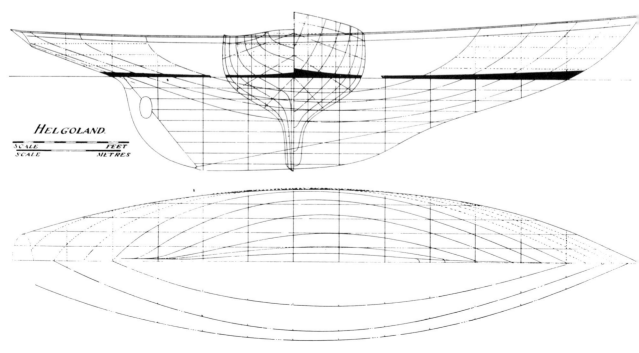

HELGOLAND.

SCALE ——— FEET
SCALE ——— METRES

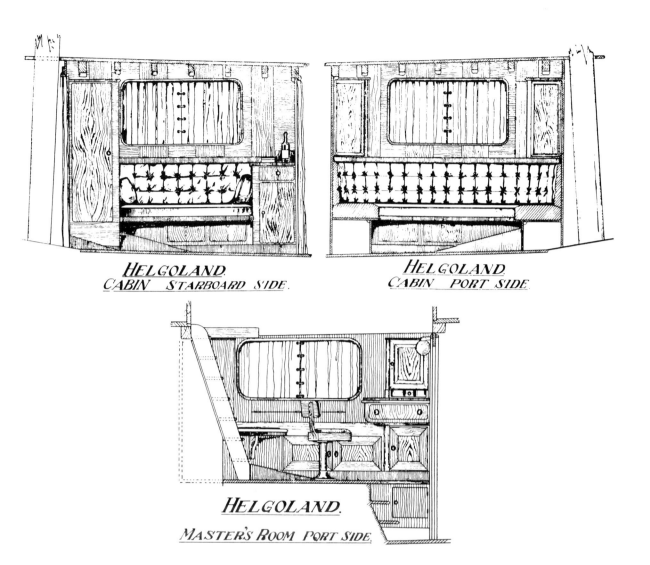

HELGOLAND.
CABIN STARBOARD SIDE.

HELGOLAND.
CABIN PORT SIDE

HELGOLAND.
MASTER'S ROOM PORT SIDE.

them the girder-like deck stringer to take the strains abreast the mast sideways as well as up and down, and two more diagonals back at the mizen.

These and many other details show great appreciation for strains and stresses set up at sea, and in *Helgoland* we have a strong workmanlike hull that can be driven without fear of her opening up through any weakness in construction details.

The accommodation plan shows that immediately abaft the fo'c'sle she has a double stateroom with a washroom at its after end. From here we go into the main cabin, which is a very cosy place, and I have often wondered that we do not make such cosy little places in our houses ashore, for this cabin, like many others, breathes a feeling of contentment and rest. One sits all the way round as there is no room to stand or walk about, so one must sit and relax, and the U-shaped settee round the table is very soothing, for everyone on it is sharing the same seat and such an arrangement

gives a spirit of friendliness to the cabin which is often lacking in houses on shore.

On the starboard side there is an ordinary sofa with a wardrobe forward, and a wine locker aft. Behind the cosy seats on either side is a sleeping berth, hidden and out of the way in the day, and yet ready for instant use, in fact as long as he did not snore a man could be asleep in this and no one know he was there, as the drawing shown of the port and starboard side will illustrate.

The port side drawing shows the U-shaped settee, and beyond it with the curtains drawn is the sleeping berth. On the left is seen the china cupboard closed, while on the right the locker door is also shut. This sleeping arrangement I have met on board the Norwegian pilot cutters where it proves most useful, as a pilot can come aboard, turn into his bunk behind the curtains, and be out of sight and mind at once.

Another drawing shows the starboard side, and here we see the full-length wardrobe at the left hand of the

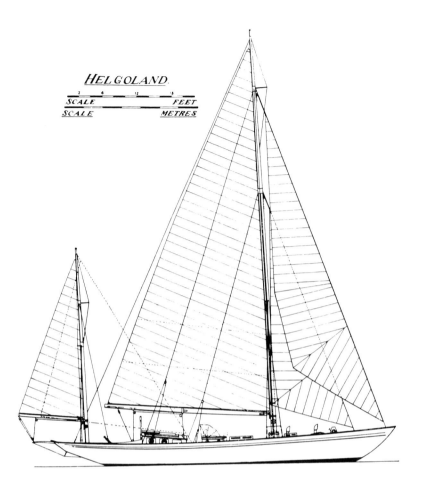

HELGOLAND.

SCALE   FEET

SCALE   METRES

bunk, while at the right hand or after end of the cabin will be seen the wine locker with a bottle, two glasses and a box of cigarettes all to hand ready for use. Such drawings as these give an idea of Henry's artistic ability, for he is able to visualise every detail of the vessels he designs and to convey this to the builders before any work is started at all.

The curtained-off bunks along the sides of the ship, like those used by the pilots, are attractive. The pilots, after all, are experienced in sleeping at sea and must have found out what is best. It is of advantage for the sleeper to be thus totally removed from the daily routine of the ship. He

might find it a little stuffy—though in cold weather this could be an advantage.

Many yachts of composite construction finished their lives with badly-rusted floors. These essential strength-members were constantly immersed in salt bilgewater, which was always present in greater or lesser quantity in any planked vessel. Opening a trap, and peering down into the murky depths, would be followed by some remark about, "... rather a lot in her", and then they resorted to the pump until it was cleared. The drive from the engine to the propeller-shaft appears to be by multiple-belt and this must have been quite advanced for those days.

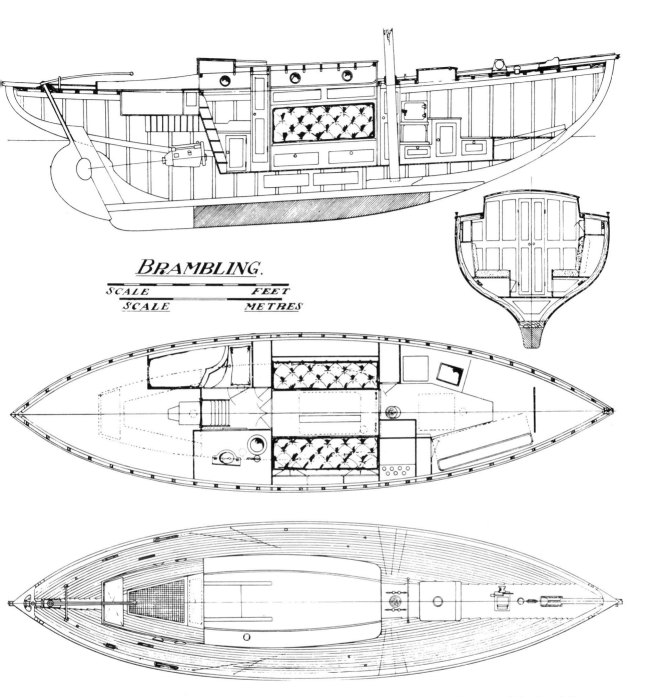

BRAMBLING.

SCALE _____ FEET

SCALE _____ METRES

Brambling

Owner, G. D. Lock
Designer, Berthon Boat Co.
Builder, Berthon Boat Co.

LOA 36 ft. 9 in. 11·201 m.
LWL 30 ft. 6 in. 9·296 m.
Beam 9 ft. 6 in. 2·895 m.
Draught 5 ft. 6 in. 1·676 m.
Displacement 10·80 tons 10·972 kilos.
Sail area 595 sq. ft. 55·27 sq. m.

Those who followed the fortunes of the Royal Ocean Racing Club's Annual Channel Race from the Solent round the *Royal Sovereign* and *Havre* Lightships and back, were not a bit surprised at *Brambling* winning this race, as in the past boats of her type have been very successful in this event. *Brambling* is a gauntlet, and the original gauntlet was second in the Channel Race in 1934 and *Greengage* (another gauntlet) won it in 1935. So we are not surprised that *Brambling* should win this year; the less so as, if we look back to the Coronation Race from the Solent to Torquay via Cherbourg and the Eddystone, we see that she saved her time on every vessel in the race.

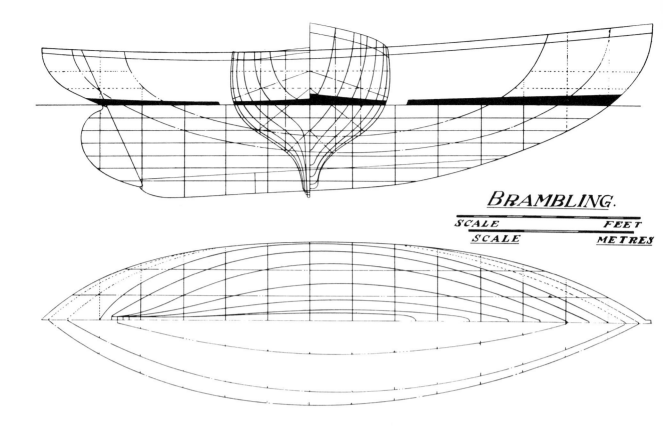

The gauntlets were designed without any thought of ocean racing, but simply to produce a good comfortable solid cruiser, one with easy draught, comfortable accommodation and easy motion in a sea, so that a man could be happy entering a shallow unfrequented creek or harbour or out at sea in a breeze of wind, yet, added to all these admirable qualities, and in no way taking away from them, we have speed, and speed enough to win places in the Channel Race more often than not.

The lines show that the gauntlet is canoe sterned with very short overhangs fore and aft, with easy and fair buttocks and water-lines, the sections making for room and comfort below decks.

The construction plan shows her long strong keel, the foregripe being connected to this with a long scarph and the sternpost by a strong sternknee, while to her $2\frac{3}{4}$ in. $\times$ $2\frac{1}{8}$ in. oak frames the pitch pine $1\frac{1}{8}$ in. planking is fastened with $\frac{1}{4}$ in. diameter copper bolts. Her decks are of teak the same thickness, while the cabin top is one inch thick, canvas covered and painted.

Her galley and pantry are abreast the mast, while forward of this is a single pipe cot in the fo'c'sle, and immediately abaft the mast comes her saloon with its

settee either side and Pulman berths above, this leading into the companionway which has a washroom to starboard and a single berthed cabin to port, her engine being tucked away under the stairway leading out on deck.

The whole of her watertight cockpit is forward of the after end of her water-line, so aboard one feels safe and sound. Because of her short overhangs *Brambling* has a small bowsprit and a bumpkin aft, the bowsprit taking the jib and the topmast stay, and the 3 ft. 9 in. bumpkin carrying the permanent topmast backstay far enough aft to clear the main boom.

The luff of the mainsail is exactly double that of the main boom, so we see that throughout *Brambling* is designed with cruising rather than with racing in view, while her jibstay, which is only 31 ft. 6 in. above the deck, just three-quarters of the mast height, makes for a snug rig. Possibly this snug rig has done more than we think for the Gauntlets in the Channel Race, for this being held at the end of July almost always takes place in a good breeze of wind when anything delicate would tend to crumple up. So in these plans of *Brambling* we see a sturdy comfortable little cruiser with speed enough to win the Channel Race.

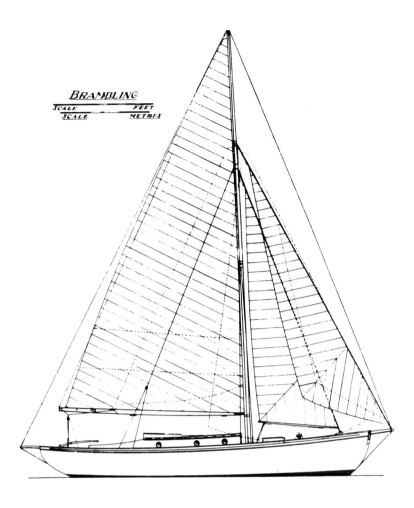

BRAMBLING

SCALE _____ FEET

SCALE _____ METRES

Designed simply as a cruising yacht, the Gauntlet did quite well in the early years of the Royal Ocean Racing Club. They were not only comfortable; but also fast enough to win. (In the 1937 Channel Race they took 1st, 3rd and 6th.)

In the post-War years, though out-classed for racing, they were still changing hands at about ten times what they cost to build in the first place. By this time most had the accommodation rearranged. Few retained the big wash-room aft. Yet what a joy it must have been to step in there and shed wet oilskins when coming off watch at midnight. The toilet-seat, and the wash-basin, occupy a prominent place in our daily routine, so why not give them space in the best part of the ship? The sliding door on this wash-room ensured an unobstructed passage for anyone

going forward. On the other hand, the two doors leading to the saloon appear odd to our eyes. I suspect they were hooked back most of the time.

The sturdy Gauntlet hull would have lent itself to long-distance voyaging, being easily slipped or laid ashore in remote places, and a husband-and-wife crew well able to cope with the handling of the yacht. They were, in fact, a good example of an all-round boat free from extremes in any direction. That these qualities were appreciated is proved by their popularity over such a long period. Such a craft will always attract admirers—even in extreme old age. It has an innate worth which the discerning will always come to, in one way or another—and so earns its place in this collection of old designs.

Andrillot

Owner, R. A. Kinnersly
Designer, Laurent Giles
Builder, A. H. Moody and Son

LOA 25 ft. 0 in. 7·62 m.
LWL 21 ft. 6 in. 6·55 m.
Beam 7 ft. 2 in. 2·184 m.
Draught 4 ft. 5 in. 1·34 m.
Displacement 4·28 tons 4,348 kilos.
Sail Area 366 sq. ft. 34 sq. m.

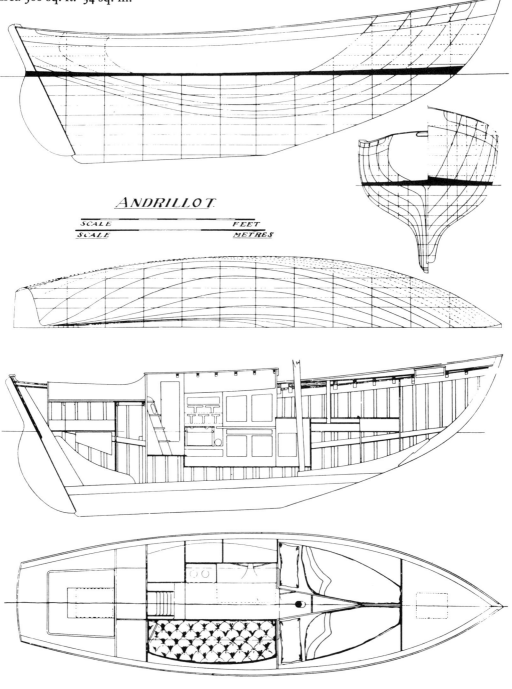

ANDRILLOT

SCALE   FEET
SCALE   METRES

This little cutter made a remarkable cruise this summer, visiting 22 ports in 23 days, her cruise taking her to the Scilly Isles, and amongst other harbours such as Brest, Benodet, Concarneau, Audierne, Lanildut, l'Abervrach, Treguier, Lézardrieux, Ile Brehat, Guernsey and Cherbourg, and when we bear in mind that she has no engine, we realise not only that she had good weather conditions for the cruise, but that she was an exceptionally fine little vessel to be able to take advantage of those conditions.

this fable when we start thinking and planning out our new ships, for these have to be carefully thought out so that they are suited to the kind of cruising we wish to do, as only then can they take us to the havens where we would be. With such thoughts in mind we turn to this 25 ft. cutter, short enough and small enough to take the owner and his wife into all the lovely little harbours they wish to visit, yet large enough to house them comfortably for the voyages they wish to make.

When we meet a transom-sterned boat with very

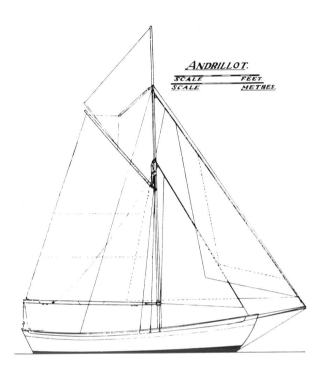

ANDRILLOT.
SCALE   FEET.
SCALE   METRES.

Often, though a vessel meets wonderful sailing conditions she is so slow or clumsy or her owner so lacks seamanship and knowledge, that the benefit of the conditions is lost, and many a vessel lost at sea or hove to in a gale of wind would have been safe in port had she had the ability to get there. Future years will see less damage through heavy weather to vessels as their good sailing qualities will have taken them into port, while a lee shore has also lost its dread because the vessels developed to-day are remarkably weatherly.

All of us remember the fable of the fox and the stork inviting each other out to dinner, and how when the stork asked the fox he had the food in the bottom of a long deep pitcher and was able to eat himself while the poor fox could not get his head into the neck at all, and when the fox asked the stork he had the food in a low flat trough so that he could gobble the food up in large mouthfuls while the stork could only peck at the food bit by bit. We who love sailing the seas must remember

little overhang forward and a gaff rig we expect to find a clumsy hull under water, but as so often happens we are deceived by the outward signs, for under water *Andrillot* has very clean lines indeed. The water-lines and buttocks being very fair, she is really a fine-bottomed boat, though as her sections will show she has been designed to give a great deal of room inside.

In the accommodation plan we see that she has no fo'c'sle as we generally think of such things in small craft, but instead has a double berthed cabin extending just abreast the mast, abaft of which a cosy cabin with settee to starboard 6 ft. 6 in. in length, and long enough and large enough to be used as a bed in case a third was carried, while to port are the dresser and chart table. At the after end of the cabin the stove, pantry and oilskin locker are arranged. One climbs up the companion way at the after end over the bridge deck and into the cockpit, the floor of which is so low that it cannot very well be self bailing.

Now this bridge deck is a fine and comforting thing in the very worst of weather, but one wonders if the owner will not in years to come abolish it (although it forms a fine sail bin) and instead have two steps up from the cabin straight into the cockpit, for this little vessel, as can be seen, is buoyant, and would very seldom ship water heavy enough into the cockpit to make the need for the bridge deck felt.

Andrillot's rudder, being hung on the stern, makes for simplicity and strength, and if anything should ever happen to such a rudder it is the simplest thing in the world to unship and reship it, and such little vessels have carried out this operation at sea.

The sail plan shows her gaff cutter rig, and the well-shaped topsail setting the whole off to perfection. The mast, it will be noticed, is well aft, and as the forestay goes to practically the stem head she has a large staysail, and the jib stay running parallel with this makes for an efficient combination of headsails.

Such a rig only needs a single crosstree, and *Andrillot* is an example of simplicity throughout. But this simplicity has been obtained without any loss of efficiency and we cease to wonder at the 850 miles cruise made by W. Barton and his wife without the aid of an engine, for *Andrillot* is a fine example of a transom-sterned gaff cutter now becoming more and more rare in spite of its low cost and upkeep.

No one guessed that *Andrillot* was to be the forerunner of all that long line of Vertues which were such a bright jewel in the English yachting scene for so many years.

After Humphrey Barton sailed *Vertue XXXV* across the Atlantic others criss-crossed back and forth, sailed round the world, round the Horn, and everywhere a boat could go. Many of these voyages were made single-handed, utilizing different types of self-steering. Vertues were bermudian-rigged, fitted with all kinds of accommodation lay-out, had self-draining cockpits, all sorts of auxiliary engines, various excrescences in the form of dog-houses arose on them, some had the topsides raised by one extra plank, they were built of every kind of timber and all over the world; but the basic hull-shape remained the same throughout. It was one of those boats which came off the designer's drawing-board quite perfect, so that nothing could be done to improve it.

At rallies in England they have mustered in considerable numbers; but on the whole have always remained the lone cruising man's choice—epitome of the sturdy boat which can go anywhere and "take it" when Father Neptune chooses to dish it out, so that the owner always has complete confidence in his craft.

Prices quoted for Vertues in later years would certainly have surprised R. A. Kinnersly, and Moodys, when *Andrillot* was built! What a simple little thing she was!—no fancy winches, no engine, no electrics, no complicated plumbing. Ah! happy days . . .

Latifa

Owner, Michael Mason
Designer, Wm. Fife & Son
Builder, Wm. Fife & Son

LOA 70 ft. 0 in. 21·33 m.
LWL 52 ft. 0 in. 15·85 m.
Beam 15 ft. 3 in. 4·72 m. **Draught** 10 ft. 2 in. 3·10 m.
Displacement 41 tons 41,656 kilos.
Sail Area 2,200 sq. ft. 204·39 sq. m.

Latifa has been a great delight to lovers of sailing vessels, for she is one of the loveliest of sailing craft yet seen, and I can see her now smoking up through the Solent with a north west breeze over her quarter, everything set even to the mizen staysail, and all her cloud of canvas seeming to lift her out of the water. She looked so airy that she reminded me of Mother Cary's chickens flitting along the tops of the waves with just their feet touching them, and the sight of her dancing over the seas that day will always live in my memory. The brightness of white sails and a white hull in strong

Latifa

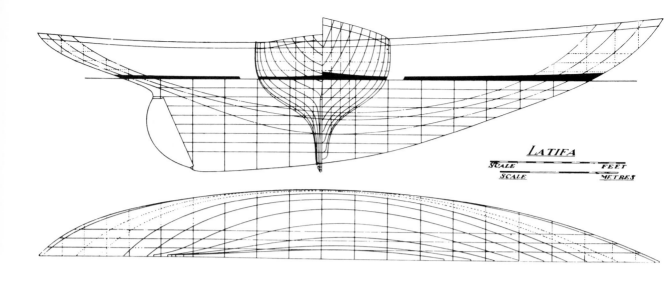

LATIFA

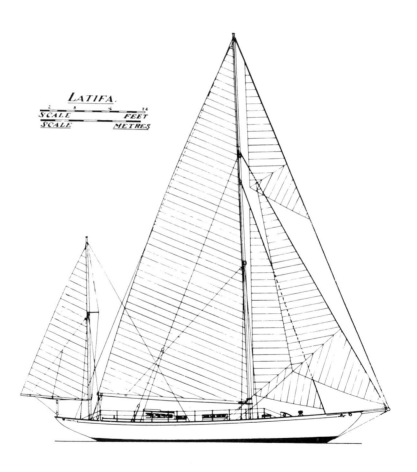

LATIFA.

sunlight is always inspiring and cheering, and when added to that we have white breaking water caused by wind strong enough to give such a vessel as *Latifa* a bone in her teeth and a long clean white wake, then we have seen a sight that is satisfying to our senses, and we feel that the world indeed is a lovely place to live in. Here before us we have the lines and plans of Michael Mason's wonderful *Latifa*, and looking at them my mind flies back to that day on which she made such a splendid picture, and one ceases to wonder that she won the Queen's Cup then, for her clean buttocks and water-lines are a delight to look upon. Her sections show she has seaworthy overhangs, the bow and stern sections being well V'd so that they will cut through

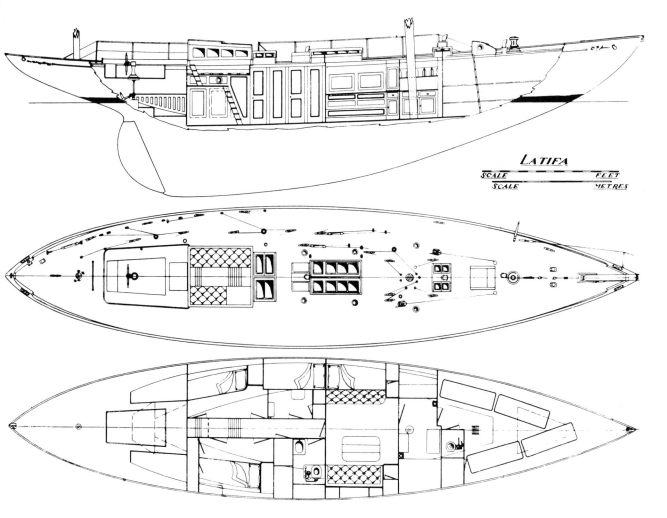

LATIFA

SCALE		FEET
SCALE		METRES

and not slam into the seas as so many do. These develop sweetly into her powerful and yet easily driven midship section, and one realises that in *Latifa* Fife has once more produced a lovely vessel, and my mind wanders back to all the wonderful yachts he has designed.

The sail plan is that of a Bermudian yawl with a three-headsail rig, and as this rig can be changed to a double-headsail rig quite easily, the owner has a great number of sail combinations in the fore triangle, to suit every wind from the lightest of airs to a gale. *Latifa*'s light weather ability can be gauged from the fact that though light winds prevailed throughout this Fastnet Race her average speed from Cowes round the Fastnet and back to the Lizard was so high; while her hard weather ability stood the owner in good stead on the way from Madeira last autumn when *Latifa* brought him safely through the worst of weather.

Boats designed and built by Fife had a magical "Rolls-Royce" quality which lifted them above the lesser breeds. The workmanship was reckoned to be unmatched anywhere.

Uffa's exuberant delight in *Latifa* is evident from his writing. Others felt the same way about her. Mention of *Latifa* imparts a legendary tone in any yachting conversation. She spanned an interesting period with one foot in the past and the other thrusting forward into the future. Immediately after the war in 1946 she sailed to Newport for the Bermuda race and this helped to prise British ocean racing out of the paralysis of the war years. She took part in the Fastnet Race as late as 1975 under Portuguese ownership.

Latifa's deck-plan is worth studying. They still relied on tackles a good deal to gain power. Possibly, in her latter years there may have been a greater preponderance of winches? The halyards and things at the foot of the main-mast appear to have been taken out to heavy cleats on the deck? Note that the life-lines are only extended along the midships portion, so that anyone who fell overboard from bow or stern would be what footballers call, "Off-Side"!

The sail plan shows quite a large area of sail, extending out beyond the overall length. It makes today's yachts appear half naked. At a later stage she set a big sail from the bowsprit end to the mast-head and an inner staysail from just inside the stemhead and this gave her a more modern look. I think the life-lines were taken further forward, too.

Ortac

Owner, Colonel C. F. King
Designer, Robert Clark
Builder, Morgan Giles

LOA 49 ft. 0 in. 14·90 m.
LWL 35 ft. 0 in. 10·66 m.
Beam 11 ft. 1 in. 3·38 m.
Draught 7 ft. 6 in. 2·29 m.
Displacement 14 tons 14·224 kilos.
Sail area 940 sq. ft. 87·30 sq. m.

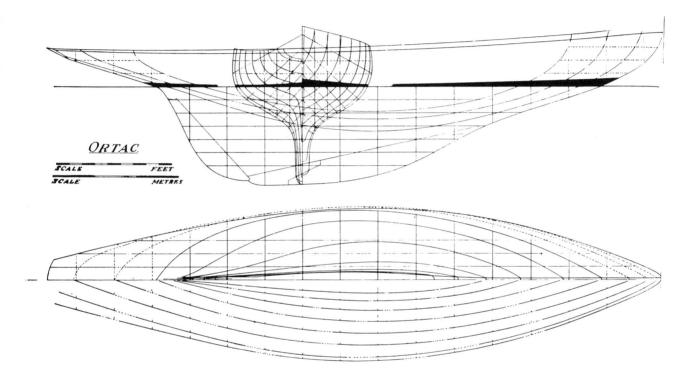

When we look at *Ortac*'s lines it is difficult to think that she is only the second boat designed by Robert Clark, his earlier boat being the cruiser *Mystery*, 26 ft. on the water-line.

Ortac is 35 ft. on the water-line, as this is the magic length for Royal Ocean Racing Club events. This length water-line enables an owner to race in either the larger or the smaller of their classes, and so gives him choice of either the Channel or the Fastnet race. There is no doubt the Royal Ocean Racing Club were wise in making a link between the two classes, this link being a boat able to enter either class, for it meant that there would be many built to the length, so forming a really keen racing class, with all the attributes of, we will say, an 8-Metre class, combined with weatherliness enough to go round the Fastnet Rock, and the comfort to be found aboard such a sized vessel. So it is not surprising that many of the ocean racers built this year were to this

length, *Ortac* being one of the most interesting of them.

The lines show a very easily driven yet powerful hull, and the more one looks at these lines and studies them the more one admires them.

The construction plan tells us that she has 45 per cent. of her total displacement in her lead keel, and this is, I think, the best proportion one could have. The mast, being well inboard, comes down on top of the fore end of the lead, so the lead keel is actually helping to make some of the downward thrust of the mainmast.

As well as her lead keel and mast being well amidships, it will be noticed that her water tanks (under the cabin floor) are also amidships. Thus with all her heavy weights in the middle *Ortac* is able to lift her bow and stern to the seas, which should make for safe and fairly dry decks.

With our present-day knowledge of construction it seems a pity that the cabin top did not run past the

Ortac *in her early ocean racing days.*

mast, and so keep full headroom at this point, for while everywhere else she has 6 ft. under beams, in way of the mast she has only 4 ft 10 in. So while her present arrangement is undoubtedly a strong and comforting one to her owner on a dark night at sea, for he knows that any side thrust of the mast is being taken directly to the powerful mast clamp fitted inside the shelf, there will be many days on which, after they have bumped their heads, his guests will wish the cabin top had been

continued past the mast. A designer is continually balancing strength and comfort in his construction plan, and only the owner can decide which he shall do.

Her accommodation plan shows that she has four berths in the main saloon. This has proved very successful, and, as can be imagined, makes for comfort and tidiness below.

The galley, though forward, is very convenient, for *Ortac* has such an easy motion that though an

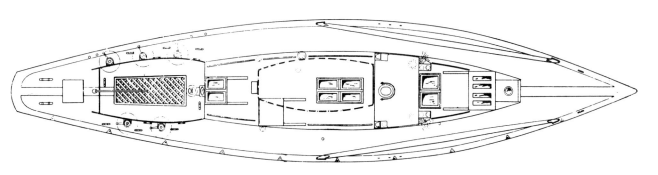

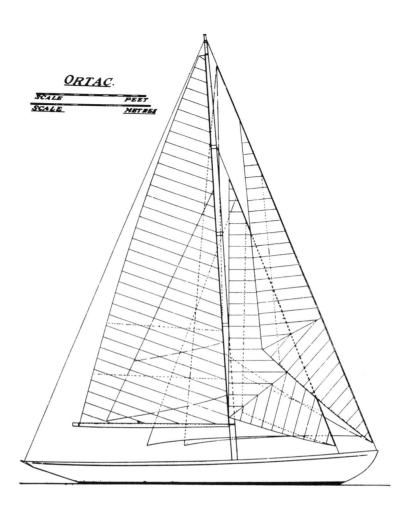

ORTAC.

SCALE _____ FEET
SCALE _____ METRES

arrangement is made for cooking aft, it was not called into use in the Heligoland Race, even when she was logging 7 knots on the wind. So the after galley has been abolished and an additional larger drawer fitted in its place.

The large forehatch enables spinnakers and headsails to be passed up and down comfortably, and, as will be seen from the deck plan, *Ortac* has been carefully thought out for ocean racing, winches and spinnaker booms, as well as the dinghy, all being placed exactly right for work at sea.

Ortac is a Bermudian cutter, and her mainmast is stepped well into her—so far, indeed, that the base of the foretriangle and the length of the mainsail on the boom are almost the same, and with her mast so far aft she should have no trouble from this in a seaway, for it is back where she is well able to carry it.

Her stemhead jib goes to the top of the mainmast, 55 ft. above the deck, while the staysail halyard is 41 ft. above the deck, the luff of the two sails being almost parallel and 4½ ft. apart, a space which enables the jib to work over the forestay fairly comfortably.

The sail plan shows she has a combination of sails to meet every kind of weather from calm to a gale, and it is not surprising that this little vessel won the Heligoland, her maiden race, without any tuning-up, in spite of the fact that such well-known ocean racers (built to the rule) as *Latifa*, *Trenchemer*, *Roland von Bremen* and *Hamburg* were ranged against her. Col. King is to be congratulated on the success of his venture, and his courage in going to a new designer has been well rewarded.

Robert Clark went on to become one of Britain's foremost designers. *Ortac*'s instant success in her first season helped to push him along this path. His work had a certain distinctive quality which enabled the more knowledgeable to eye a newcomer to some crowded anchorage and say: "Looks like a Robert Clark boat." One always has the feeling that he is an artist, as well as being a designer.

Ortac carried a rudimentary pulpit, before this fitting had become widespread. Her fore-triangle, too, portrayed her designer's forward-looking thoughts. Working sails were being set from the mast-head. In former years only fine-weather "kites" were carried there, because the separate top-mast was light and flimsy. Even the first one-piece masts for bermudian rig had a very slender upper section. Now, they were being stiffened up—right to the top. The mast was also moving back aft to throw more emphasis on the fore-triangle. Mast-head spinnakers were coming in, (and many a racing skipper staring in fascinated horror at its antics in a hard breeze has had cause to rue the day!)

There was still argument about the proper position for the galley? Again, I must say I think the size of these yachts refuted many of the points against having it up forward. Now that boats have shrunk, along with our pockets, there is no longer any question but that it is better aft.

Ortac was a fine yacht and she helped to initiate all the new ideas which were being bandied about then. She remains actively sailed by a sailing school in Germany and raced at Cowes in the 1970s. I expect Robert Clark remembers her with affection. And so should we all—as we study her beauteous lines.

Zeearend

Owner, C. Bruynzeel, Jnr.
Designer, Olin of Sparkman & Stephens
Builder, De Vries Lentsch, Jnr.

LOA 54 ft. 7½ in. 16·649 m.
LWL 40 ft. 0 in. 12·192 m.
Beam 12 ft. 0 in. 3·658 m.
Draught 8 ft. 4 in. 2·54 m.
Displacement 45,260 lb. 20·528 kilos.
Sail area 1,380 sq. ft. 128·20 sq. m.
Lead Keel 19,260 lb. 8·617 kilos.

As usual Olin has drawn a wonderfully sweet and fair set of lines for *Zeearend*, and we cannot but help being struck by the easy sweeping diagonal lines of this ocean racer, while her water-lines and buttocks all give an impression of speed. The sections, while giving the same impression, also tell of a comfortable boat at sea, so once again we see that Olin has combined speed, seaworthiness and comfort in a remarkable way, and one can see that *Zeearend* is a boat that would always have to be reckoned with in an ocean race, no matter what the weather conditions were.

She has two pipe cots in her fo'c'sle, and immediately abaft this is a double berthed cabin abreast the mainmast taking the full width of the ship, abaft of which are two single cabins, one to port and one to starboard. At the after end of the starboard cabin is the washroom. Next aft comes one of the most unusual arrangements yet seen afloat, for the galley is arranged to starboard, while to port is the pantry, and two winding stairs, one on either side, leading out to the deck; between them one walks straight into the dining saloon, where the circular seats are arranged around a round table. Though these round tables are getting rare it is difficult to think of anything more companionable, for, sitting at a round table, one is able to see the faces of all without bending and leaning forward, and such a table takes one's mind back to King Arthur and his knights. There being no head to a round table there can be no thought of one man occupying a better seat than another, and one would like to see round tables used more than at present.

The arrangement proved so comfortable and cosy that we see a similar edition of it in Dudok van Heel's *Tromp II*, though in his case he has made the table square.

Abaft this is the watertight cockpit and the mizen mast.

Like most ocean racers designed these days *Zeearend* has a yawl rig, and looking at her rig and the rigs of practically every ocean racer, whether American,

Original caption: Zeearend, *the winner, has two tucked under her lee at the start.*

German, Dutch or any other nationality, our mind goes back to a few years ago when there were a great many arguments, as there always will be, on the rig for sea work.

The cutter rig is undoubtedly the fastest, and therefore the best whenever it can be used, but this rig is penalised, and quite rightly, because of its efficiency; and so, as the next best thing, everyone goes for a yawl rig because of its allowance. These yawls are practically the same as we have used in British waters for a great many years, and have proved to be very good rigs for sea work as well as being fast, for they have the advantage of what we used to call a short boomed cutter rig, and added to this a mizen mast and mizen staysail given practically free under the rule. If one deplores the fact that America has forsaken her schooner rig for the British yawl rig, one must take comfort in the fact that here at least a point which has been argued about for many years has been proved, that point being "Which is the better rig, the yawl or the schooner?" for the yawl has proved so efficient at sea that all American designers have dropped the schooner rig in favour of it in spite of the fact that the Bermudian yawl rates at 98 per cent. and the schooner at only 92 per cent. But for all that the schooner rig has still much to recommend it and will always be seen upon the sea.

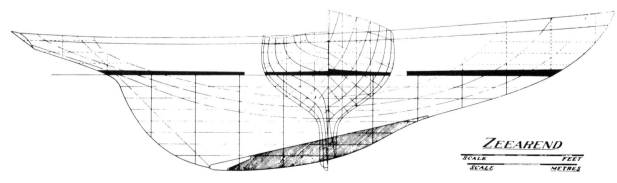

ZEEAREND

SCALE FEET
SCALE METRES

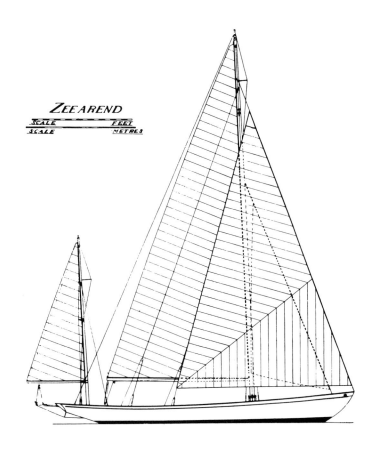

The name "Bruynzeel" was to figure prominently in ocean racing over a very long period. In 1949 his hard-chine light-displacement *Zeevalk*, de-signed by Van De Stadt, caused quite a stir.

Zeearend was another large yawl from the board of Olin Stephens; but built in Holland. She

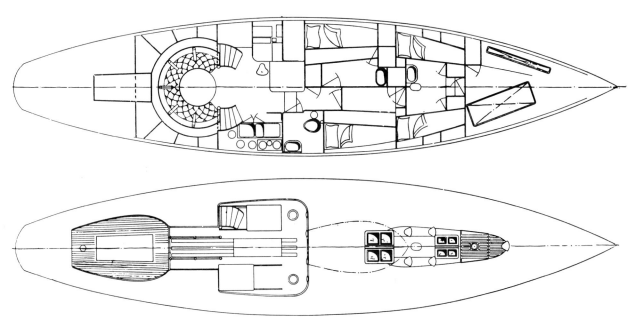

won the 1937 Fastnet and had many other successes. The fore-triangle was what we would now call "seven-eighths" and it has recently been revived. It looks as though two sets of runners were used to support the main-mast.

The round table shown in the accommodation plan was a novel little concept, but rather wasteful of space I would have thought, and the table-top, itself, small for six people to eat off. The two curved stairways continued the circular theme and were really quite unusual. Twin main hatches have been fitted to other yachts though. The idea was to get some of the large racing crew forward out of the cockpit for trimming; but this can scarcely have been so for *Zeearend*. I have never been shipmates with this arrangement myself and cannot say whether there are advantages which outweigh the added complication and expense. Perhaps one could be reserved for persistent "companionway-crouchers", leaving the other free for actual use?

The fleet which came to the line for the 1937 Fastnet included American, Dutch, German, British and French yachts—so *Zeearend*'s win was well-earned. The other boat in the race to Olin Stephens' design, *Elizabeth MacCaw*, took the cup for first home. He had now designed the winner in all four Fastnets in which he had been concerned.

Golden Eye

Owner, H. Prescott Wells
Designer, Phil Rhodes of Cox & Stevens Inc.
Builder, Minneford Yacht Yard Inc.

LOA 41 ft. 3 in. 12·56 m.
LWL 30 ft. 0 in. 9·14 m.
Beam 11 ft. 0 in. 3·35 m.
Draught 6 ft. 0 in. 1·82 m.
Displacement 10·11 tons 10,261 kilos.
Sail area 917 sq. ft. 85·18 sq. m.

Though designed as a comfortable and sensible cruiser, or perhaps because of this, and because of the fact that her designer was Phil Rhodes, *Golden Eye* has turned out to be a wonderful little sailer, one that is able to ghost along in very light weather, and when the breeze has blown up and the weather is bad she is not only fast but comfortable.

As can be seen from her dimensions she is beamy, and at the same time of heavier displacement than usual these days, these two things making for comfort below

decks and also comfort and safety at sea. It would be difficult to improve upon the lines of this little craft, a fact proved by her coming out top of her class in the Gibson Island race. A study of her lines will prove interesting and instructive to all, for she is another little cruiser of which Phil Rhodes may justly feel very proud.

The construction plan shows that the deckhouse, which gives her the unusual head room of 6 ft. 5 in., runs forward past the mast in order to give full head room in the double-berthed fo'c'sle cabin, but we see there is no weakness arising from this, for like the rest of her construction the strains and stresses have been thought of and prepared for.

Her accommodation plan shows that where one usually sees two pipe cots in the fo'c'sle, she has two built-in berths, and the fo'c'sle really becomes a double-berthed forward cabin, abaft of which she has a roomy galley and pantry to port, while to starboard is her washroom and farther aft her main cabin with built-in berths behind the two settees, so that below decks *Golden Eye* is a cosy little ship.

A companion way leads out of the after hatch over the bridge deck to the cockpit, and under this her

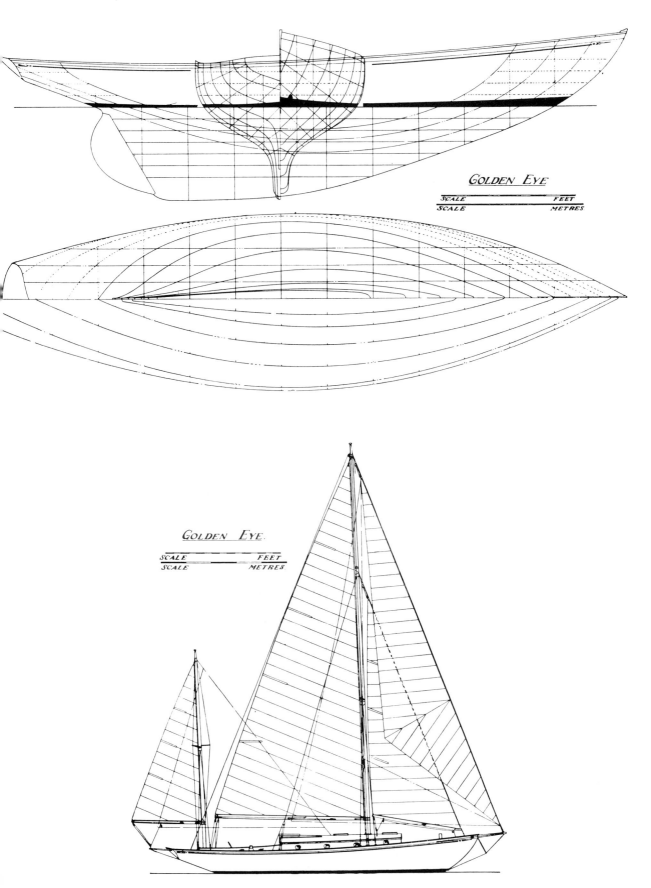

GOLDEN EYE

SCALE ——————— FEET
SCALE ——————— METRES

GOLDEN EYE.

SCALE ——————— FEET
SCALE ——————— METRES

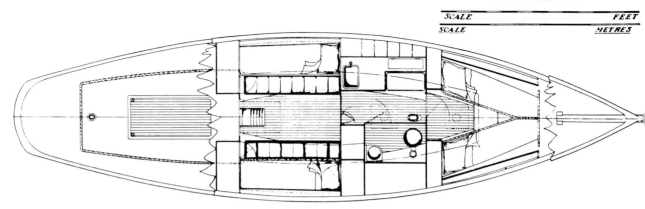

auxiliary engine is fitted, and while this is partitioned off from the accommodation it is quite accessible.

Her sail plan shows she has a double headsail yawl rig, which enables her to set combinations of sail to suit every kind of weather from the lightest air to a gale of wind, and the rig seems perfect for such a little cruiser. There is only one small point I should like to see changed, and that is that the mizen staysail be tacked to the after end of the deckhouse, for my experience has been that to be really efficient the mizen staysail must not go forward of a point half-way between the main and mizen masts, as if it does it is fighting with the mainsail and the two spoil each other. In *Golden Eye* we see a perfect little cruiser with speed enough in her to win long distance races under any conditions.

In his introduction to the book, Uffa quoted *Golden Eye* as an example of "the state of perfection reached by the cruising racer of today". Certainly her pedigree was of the highest as Phil Rhodes was a leading designer for many years, while Minneford's remains one of the very few top yards in the U.S., which can build a 12-metre. This kind of yawl rig remained popular in American waters until the advent of the IOR in the early 1970s. The mizen looks only just enough to overcome the windage of its own mast and rigging. But off the wind it counted, with its mizen staysail: two masted yachts also benefited from the rule of the Cruising Club of America. Note that Uffa calls this forty-one footer, a 'little cruiser'.

30 Square Metres

Waterwitch

Owner, Geo. Wansbrough
Designer, Knud H. Reimers
Builder, Uffa Fox

LOA 43 ft. 6 in. 13·25 m.
LWL 28 ft. 6 in. 8·68 m.
Beam 7 ft. 2 in. 2·18 m.
Draught 4 ft. 11 in. 1·50 m.
Displacement 2·75 tons 2,794 kilos.
Sail Area 323 sq. ft. 30 sq. m.

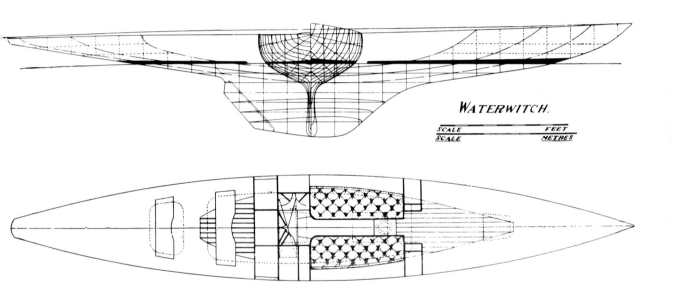

WATERWITCH.

SCALE   FEET
SCALE   METRES

After a great deal of thought and hesitation the 30-square metre class has at last started in British waters, for one Sunday late in the summer of 1937, George Wansbrough, as the first passenger of a new air line, flew from London to the Isle of Wight, and as he was the first and only one it was agreed that the plane should fly over a certain field in Cowes, and if he signalled take him back to London. And that is exactly what happened. George hailing his aeroplane reminded me very much of the same chap hailing a taxi in London, and so this day saw the start of the 30-square metres in British waters.

I have always been a believer in the Skerry Cruiser classes, for their rules produce a fast type of craft that gives a great deal of pleasure to those sailing it, and also at the same time they produce a very sturdy little vessel, one that is both strong and seaworthy as the lines and construction plan of *Waterwitch* clearly show. So seaworthy are these little boats that the water-line length 28 ft. 6 in. was chosen, as it would enable them to take part in the races across channel under the Royal Ocean Racing Club's rules to such ports as St. Malo and Oistrehem, etc., and it is probable that these little vessels will do a great deal of this type of racing. The hull rates very badly by the rule, but as the sail area to drive it is so small it levels things up, and the Royal Ocean Racing Club rule seems so well balanced that these craft, though not being designed at all to this rule, will nevertheless rate fairly under it, so that their chance of success is no greater or less than the more normal type of vessel.

The lines are those of a normal 30-square metre, long and easily driven, while her keel is kept down to the minimum length allowed by the rule. The sail plan is to the maximum height allowed, for while a few years ago we were allowed to increase the height of sail plan as long as punishments were taken, it was decided to put the limit at 12·70 metres and therefore we have a

The 30-square metre, Waterwitch *beating down the Solent.*

proportion of three and half times the main boom for the luff of the sail, which gives a very efficient shaped sail for windward work.

Once it was known that a 30-square metre had been ordered for racing on the Solent, several people who had wanted one now decided to build to the class, and while some were ordered in England others were put in hand in Sweden, so that soon there were half a dozen being built, enough to ensure the future of the class. The Skerry Cruisers with their liveliness and buoyant hulls are a type that appeal to many people, and it would seem now the class has been started in British waters it will prosper and grow. The following cable, though short, tells a great deal, namely, that two British 30-square metres will be racing in American waters at the end of next summer, and it is hoped that some

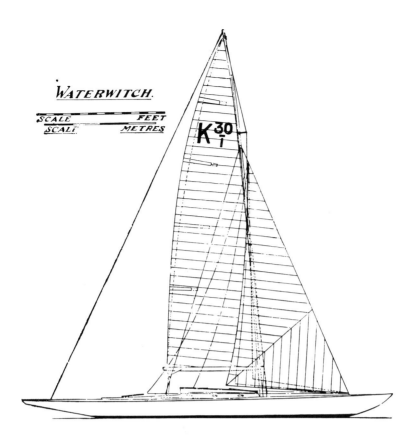

WATERWITCH.

SCALE ⎯⎯⎯⎯ FEET
SCALE ⎯⎯⎯⎯ METRES

K $\frac{30}{1}$

Scandinavian "thirties" will be going across too, and that these will race at Cowes during The Week on their way out to America.

Sent October 5, 1937.

COMMODORE, Beverly Yacht Club,
53 State St., Boston, Mass.
Can you please accept challenge for Team Races next summer in 30-square metres. Suggest five races between August 15 and 27. Two boat teams to represent each country. UFFA FOX, Cowes, England.

After the war Colonel "Blondie" Hasler bought the Thirty Square Metre *Tre Sang* and converted her for ocean racing. He contrived two bunks for himself and his crew, a gimballed stove, chart space, hanging for oilskins, sail racks and warp stowage. The mainsail he had recut with a higher foot, added a topping lift, scrapped the biggest genoa, and moved the backstay further aft so as to be able to carry a dinghy there. In 1946 he won the small class championship of the RORC with her and placed Third on points in the whole fleet, as only *Maid of Malham* and *Lara* had more. People said only iron-bound men could have driven her through a season of offshore racing; but "Blondie" disclaimed any undue hardship. (Which school of thought would you believe?)

After that *Tre Sang* passed into the hands of Commander "Bill" King. When I was with him in 1949, aboard his new RNSA 24 *Galway Blazer*, we lay alongside *Tre Sang* off Camper and Nicholson's Yard at Gosport. Bill jocularly referred to the pair as his fleet of yachts. I used to look at that long, narrow tooth-pick of a boat, now rather tatty, and her permanently-bent mast, as though she had got stuck under a low bridge. Now in the late seventies there is a revival of this type of yacht in Scandinavia at least.

One-design Classes

This chapter is written in an effort to assist, for the owners of one-designs would be very grateful if the IYRU could find it possible to foster and encourage one-design class racing. Generally speaking, the IYRU has mainly encouraged building to formulas or restrictions, and might be said to have taken little interest in one-design classes, for though the Union has adopted the 12-square metres and the monotypes, and years ago an International 12-ft. dinghy class, these are exceptions, and with no one to guide them the various clubs round the coasts of all countries have developed their own local one-designs. While these have given a great deal of pleasure they would give even more if there were fewer classes and they were international, so that a man racing in Ireland, another in Scotland and a third in the Solent, could ship his one-design, say, over to Stockholm or Oslo and spend a holiday racing against the Scandinavians and other nations, or that a man from the Thames Estuary could spend a summer's holiday with his one-design racing in the clear blue waters of the West Country, say, at Falmouth. Now we have only to look in *Lloyd's Register* to read of over 150 different one-design classes in British waters, and generally speaking, there are only about 12 of each class, and they are only raced in the one harbour.

It will be said that this is brought about because the conditions vary so much. But there is a great deal of nonsense talked about local conditions; for instance, a Swedish and Finnish 6-metre challenged for the Scandinavian Gold Cup and went across to America after it, and the three contestants each won two races in the contest, so that the full seven races had to be sailed before the American finally won the trophy. Yet these three boats were developed under entirely different conditions, and varied accordingly. The truth of it is that boats are driven by wind and float on the water, and wherever there is water and wind the conditions throughout the year must be very similar, the only big difference there can be is in the depth of water. The Scandinavians are blest with deep water, and indeed most places where people sail have good depth, though every so often we have a shallow harbour like Bembridge with a sturdy and strong sailing club, where a shallow-draught racer is needed similar to the Redwing class, which is included in this chapter, as such a class should be borne in mind.

So far I have only considered racing on coasts, but there should be a class for inland waters, and if it is a centreboard class it becomes cheap to run as the boats can be hauled in and out of the water without any difficulty; there is the further advantage that they are a lively and exciting type of craft to sail, whereas to sail a heavy-keeled boat on inland waters is not exciting enough. My own personal view is that the IYRU would be doing a great deal of good if they could adopt and recommend a series of International One-Design classes, for they would be encouraging and helping another class of sailors whom so far they have neglected.

The problem is full of difficulties, but as some of the finest brains in the yachting world are on the Council, these could be overcome.

First of all the classes to be adopted are very difficult to decide upon, as it is important that the best types of craft should be encouraged; then another point is that as this is an international body the designs must come from as many countries as possible, so that there is no feeling in any one country that she is being left out.

I believe that the one-design classes should range from somewhere round 40 ft. water-line down to the 20-square metre centreboard inland racer, and it would seem that the best way of arriving at the selection of designs would be to say that America and Britain have, generally speaking, developed fast seaworthy cruisers above 25 ft. on the line, that the Scandinavian countries, generally speaking, produced wonderfully cheap and fast one-designs around the 6-metre size, and that Central Europe has specialised in inland-water classes, and therefore that we should choose racers from 30 to 40 ft. water-line from Britain or America, and from 18 to 25 ft. water-line from Scandinavian countries, and a centreboard inland racer from Central Europe. Those are the lines on which I have developed this chapter. In *Stormy Weather*, *Evenlode* and *Golden Eye* we have three lovely little vessels fast enough to give a great deal of fun even when sailed in day races, and sturdy enough to take their owners round the world if they so wished, and in them we have the finest types of racing cruisers, while the smaller one-design classes are all excellent examples of the day cruisers, *Ferret* showing the type of craft developed for inland racing.

A careful study of all these plans and the problems will help us all towards the correct solution of the problem, for the examples given are as fine as can be found in this world. Supposing *Evenlode* or a similar vessel designed by Fife was chosen as a 35 ft. water-line class; then a committee of British yachtsmen and designers would be formed to control and settle all points arising from this class, just as the Scandinavian countries now control the Dragons; and if the light and lively 15-square metre was chosen as a smaller class this too would be controlled by the Scandinavian Committee, while the inland waters class would be in the hands of a committee from Central Europe. Possibly a corresponding member from each country should be elected to all these committees, as then he would collect the thoughts from his country and pass them on to the committee, while the committee would send him an outline of any proposed change for his and his country's views on it; for we all know that a single International Committee would be too big and cumbersome to deal with the problems arising.

If a range of one-design classes from 40 ft. water-line downwards could be adopted and fostered by the

IYRU and the North American Yacht Racing Union, it would save a great deal of trouble to clubs, for they would naturally adopt an International one-design class, and the state of affairs that at present exists at Lowestoft be done away with. For at Lowestoft there was a move to start a one-design class, and now they have two Dragons, two Tumlarens and two Star boats, all six racing together on a handicap basis, whereas had there been an international class they would have adopted it and they would have had six boats to one class which would have given good sport. So one hopes that the IYRU will see its way through the difficult problem of adopting a range of one-design classes as International One-Designs, for though this would mean a great deal of work for them the good which would arise from it would be well worth it.

Three craft, designed as cruisers and for ocean racing, head the designs put forward to enable us to study the question of International One-Design classes, and these three are 40, 35 and 30 ft. on the water-line. The difference in these lengths is sufficient to give different size craft that need different crews, and in which different accommodation plans are arranged.

The first of these is *Stormy Weather*, whose plans I have taken from my *Second Book* to illustrate this chapter. When we remember that in 1935 she won the transatlantic race from Brenton Reef, America, to Bergen in Norway, a distance of 3000 miles, after which she sailed down to Cowes and then won our Fastnet Race on her way home to America, finally sailing to windward across the Atlantic in the remarkable time of 23 days, we realise what an excellent little vessel *Stormy Weather* is, and what a wonderful class would be formed if there were a dozen or so such craft. They are so fast that they would give a great deal of pleasure for day sailing, and their accommodation is such that they would make wonderful cruisers and wonderful little vessels for passage races.

Some of the boats mentioned above are not in these pages, by reason of space and selection. Only after World War 2 did Europe copy the American way of sailing and develop one-design classes on a continental (and subsequently international) scale. The IYRU always thought in terms of the metre boats, epitomized by the 6-metre class. Even in the late 1940s, the IYRU established cruiser-racer metre boats and the 5.5-metre. But only a few were ever built; sailors built offshore racing boats to the CCA, RORC and equivalent offshore rules, while the great explosion in centreboarders was in mass produced plywood and glass fibre one-designs.

Lake One-design

Designer, Philip Rhodes of Cox & Stevens Inc.

LOA 34 ft. 0 in. 10·36 m.
LWL 23 ft. 4 in. 7·11 m.
Beam 7 ft. 9 in. 2·36 m.
Draught 5 ft. 3 in. 1·60 m.
Sail area 444 sq. ft. 41·24 sq. m.

This class came into being as the great lakes badly needed a one-design class that could be handled by two, and was economical in cost and upkeep, and which, at the same time, would be fast and seaworthy. It was intended that the class should be manly enough to take part in the long distance racing on the lakes, and the formation of it was tackled in an admirable manner.

Major W. F. N. Windier, of the Royal Canadian Yacht Club, appointed the committee, representing the ten Canadian and American Yacht clubs in the Lake Racing Association, of which he is president, to promote the class.

The committee is formed from the following clubs:

Buffalo Yacht Club.	Crescent Yacht Club.
Kingston Yacht Club.	Olcott Yacht Club.
Oswego Yacht Club.	Queen City Yacht Club.
Rochester Yacht Club.	Royal Canadian Yacht
Royal Hamilton Yacht	Club.
Club.	Youngstown Yacht Club.

After carefully studying a number of designs by the best Canadian and American architects, they finally selected this design by Philip Rhodes of Cox & Stevens, and looking at the plans, we heartily agree with their choice. The lines tell of a fast, yet weatherly and seaworthy hull. The construction plan shows that it is one that will give no anxiety when the wind is strong and the sea is running high, for the mahogany planking is just on $\frac{7}{8}$ in. in thickness, and the frames only 8 in. apart.

A study of the construction plan will show that the designer has carefully considered all the stresses and strains put upon such a vessel. With no less than five feet headroom, she has a cosy cabin, the transoms of which enable three to sleep in comfort, one to port and two to starboard, while the galley and pantry is situated at the farther end of the cabin on the port side, which is, without doubt, the best place for it in such a craft, for here the motion is least, and cooking can be carried on at sea, and also the fumes from cooking quickly escape out of the hatchway, which can nearly always be left open, while the forehatch generally has to remain closed.

Under the ladder, the Sea Scout engine is installed out of the way, where it can easily be reached when needed.

The deck of this boat is fairly clear, and there is practically no need for anyone to go out of the

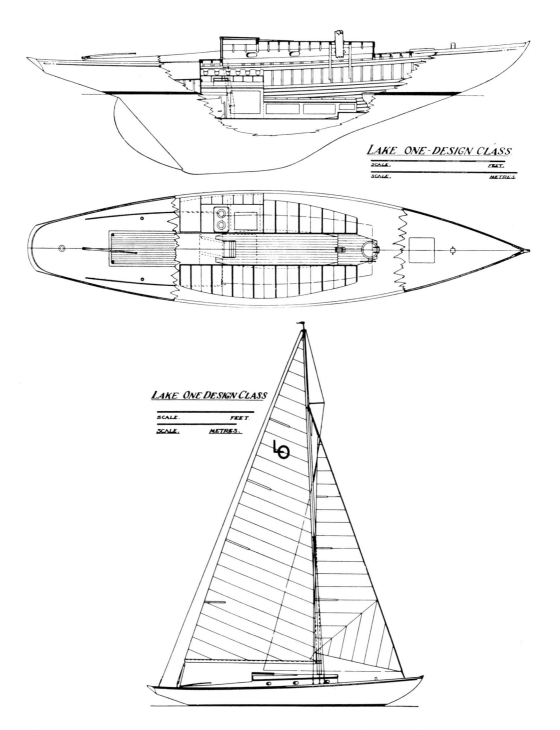

LAKE ONE-DESIGN CLASS

SCALE.   FEET.

SCALE.   METRES.

LAKE ONE DESIGN CLASS

SCALE.   FEET.

SCALE.   METRES.

watertight cockpit when once she is under way, as all sheets and runner falls lead back here.

The 444 square feet of sail area is well arranged, as one-quarter of it is in the headsail, and the other three parts in the mainsail, which brings the mast well aft, a point which makes for a well-behaved boat in a seaway, and one which will tend to ride quietly at her anchor. So we see that these little vessels have a great deal to recommend them. Looking at their plans, I am reminded of two French yachtsmen from St. Malo,

who came to Cowes to talk over a one-design class with me. They wanted a fast little sailing craft that was manly enough to take them through the strong tidal waters from St. Malo to Guernsey and back. This class would seem to suit them, as they are speedy and seaworthy, and have cabin accommodation and cooking arrangements that would enable the racers to live aboard, and spend nights at sea if necessary, in comfort and safety.

Dragons

Designer, Johan Anker

LOA 29 ft. 2 in. 8·88 m.
LWL 18 ft. 7 in. 5·66 m.
Beam 6 ft. 3 in. 1·90 m.
Draught 3 ft. 9⅝ in. 1·16 m.
Sail area 215 sq. ft. 20 sq. m.

The Dragons, without ever being officially formed into one, have developed into what is in effect a strong and vigorous International One-Design class. They have the great advantage of being controlled by the country of their design, and so problems that arise can be settled quickly and easily. Every class in the world is bound to have problems arising from time to time, which often need a quick settlement, and the reason for the Dragons increasing in popularity and spreading to so

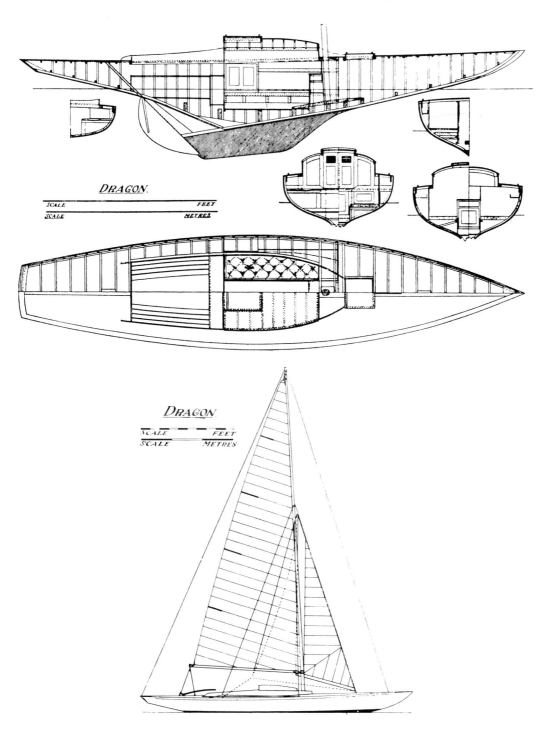

DRAGON.

SCALE   FEET
SCALE   METRES

DRAGON.

SCALE   FEET
SCALE   METRES

many countries, is that they are undoubtedly fine little racers and day cruisers, and at the same time are very cheap, for Johan Anker, being a builder, has designed a type of craft that is very easily and cheaply constructed, yet one that at the same time is fast and seaworthy and a great pleasure to sail. These points are exactly what is required in a one-design class, for the whole point of a one-design class is to have boats that are inexpensive, and so do away with designing and building competition. These boats should be cheap to buy and run, and yet they should be boats any man would be proud to own and enjoy sailing in. The Dragons seem to fulfil all these points, and are now to be found in a great many countries in strong numbers, there being no less than seventy of them in British waters.

Looking at the plans we see that on a very fast set of lines Johan Anker has produced a fine little vessel with cabin accommodation, driven by a Bermudian cutter rig, a low fore triangle making for cheapness, as only one pair of crosstrees is needed to support the mast.

The topmast stay prevents the top of the mast from going aft, while the permanent topmast backstay on the counter keeps it from bending forward; throughout simplicity has been aimed at, and because the Dragons have the qualities sought for in one-design classes they will continue and prosper.

It is difficult to believe, now, that Johan Anker originally conceived the Dragon as a cruiser/racer. Later, and particularly after they achieved Olympic status, the cabin became vestigial. That they are able to continue racing in quite rough conditions may be a reflection of their origins, though. Some old Dragons have finished out their days cruising.

Uffa's remarks about how cheap they are to buy and run will echo hollowly for anyone who has had to do with Dragons in recent years!

The Bjarne Aas Class

Designer, Bjarne Aas

LOA 33 ft. 4 in. 10·15 m.
LWL 21 ft. 5 in. 6·55 m.
Beam 6 ft. 9 in. 2·05 m.
Draught 5 ft. 4 in. 1·60 m.
Displacement 6,950 lb. 3,152 kilos.
Sail area 418 sq. ft. 38·85 sq. m.

There is no doubt that these boats are lovely little vessels. We have only to look at the lines to realise their speed, and those of us who have seen them sailing have been filled with admiration for them. The cabin enables them to be used as cruisers by any owner wishing to do so, and so it is not surprising that this class is growing in popularity. There is a large fleet of them already established on Long Island Sound, where they have given good sport, while another fleet has been formed in Bermuda, and F. G. Mitchell, the Commodore of the Royal Corinthian, is starting a fleet of them on the Crouch. As we look at them under way and their plans we realise that with their 6 ft. 9 in. beam they represent very closely the type of vessel we all hoped the 6-metre rule would produce, and so one might almost call this class a cruising type of 6-metre, and as such they have great appeal.

The sail plan is well but simply stayed under two pairs of crosstrees and a pair of jumper struts. These, with a permanent backstay aft, are sufficient to hold this rig in place, and designers, builders and rule makers may learn a great deal from a careful study of these plans.

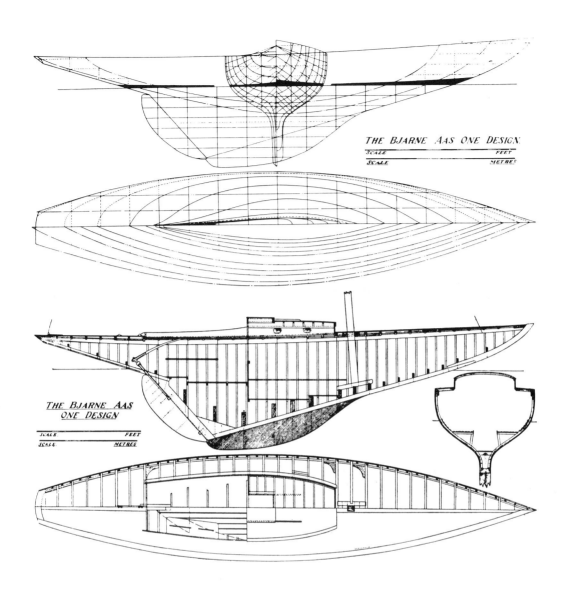

THE BJARNE AAS ONE DESIGN

SCALE _____ FEET
SCALE _____ METRES

THE BJARNE AAS
ONE DESIGN

SCALE _____ FEET
SCALE _____ METRES

*The class became
known as the
International One-
Design and is still
(1978) racing. Fleets
grew up in Norway,
Bermuda, England and
Long Island Sound.*

INTERNATIONAL 14 FOOTERS
Thunder

Owner, Peter Scott
Designer, Uffa Fox
Builder, Uffa Fox

LOA 14 ft. 0 in. 4·26 m.
LWL 13 ft. 9 in. 4·19 m.
Beam 4 ft. 8¼ in. 1·42 m.
Draught 8 in. and 5 ft. 2 in.
  0·2 m. and 1·57m.
Displacement 800 lb. 362 kilos.
Sail Area 125 sq. ft. 11·61 sq. m.

One of the most difficult things in this world is to convince people making rules for different classes that weight is bad. On all sides rule makers think that heavy weight is the cure for all ills in yacht design and proportion, and this in spite of the fact that one can never pick up a newspaper without seeing an advertisement on the best method to reduce our own weight. I have always argued that the only place where weight is of any use is in a steam roller, and have very seldom been listened to. I think the reason is that when there were no rules requiring a minimum displacement, boats were undoubtedly built too light, and though they gave wonderful sport they did not last long, and so made the game of yacht racing expensive. At the same time long low overhangs also came into being, and these very light and weak hulls with their overhangs left behind them the impression that overhangs were bad and lightness too was bad, and that the only thing makers of rules had to do to ensure good vessels was to continually increase the weight and discourage overhangs, the result being that this form of religion has taken a very firm hold.

Latterly it has been proved beyond doubt that moderate overhangs, because they increase the ability of a vessel in a seaway by increasing her fore and aft stability, are good; and we are slowly learning that weight in itself is very bad, as it tends to make the craft into half-tide rocks, that are dead and lifeless to sail, and very wet in a seaway. We have instances of this in the small-metre classes, the "sixes" and "eights", for in the 6-metres 80 per cent. of the displacement is in the ballasted lead keel, which shows the result of people pinning their faith to heavy weights in rule formulae.

Ten years ago I built the 14-footer *Avenger*, and her planking was $\frac{5}{32}$ in. full in total thickness. In her we won 57 prizes in 57 starts, and I sailed her across the Channel to Havre to take part in the regatta there in 1928, and then sailed back again to Cowes. And this year, ten years after she was built, I sailed her at Lowestoft, as the winds there were too light for her owner who weighs 23 stone, and she is in even better condition to-day than she was when new. Here is conclusive proof that she was quite strong enough; and yet in the past ten years the weight of 14-footers has been increased so much that last year we were using double the thickness of planking ($\frac{5}{16}$ in. full) all because the rule makers had increased the hull weights so much through these years. The result was that we were getting to a boat that seldom planed, and the dinghies that plane are lovely boats to sail as they are flat floored which gives initial stability, and they are very lively little chaps.

It was all very well to go on with this type of boat when we were racing amongst ourselves (the heavy flat-floored boat, that should, but seldom could, plane because of the weight in her), but last year the Canadians were sending over a team of boats, which I knew would be of the planing type such as I had developed, and which have the same spars and rig, but as they would be lighter they would plane away from our craft on the days in which we had breezes in which to plane. Because our increased weight had made planing a rare occurrence I designed a sharp-floored boat that would not plane but would, however, knife her way along to windward where she would be very fast and would also run well, but which would never plane or reach at all fast in a breeze, and then hoped that these contests would show a great deal of windward and running work and very little reaching in planing speeds. So the weight in the rule had forced me to go to an undesirable type. The midship section of *Daybreak*, Peter Scott's last year's 14-footer, shows this type of craft, and we can see from it that she is very tender and 'tiply', but very easily driven fast to windward and running, and slow in reaching; and as the contest against the Canadians was held in a wind so light that they had no advantage at all from their lighter hulls, *Daybreak* had a second and two firsts in the five races against them.

Once the Dinghy Committee had seen where the excessive weight rule was taking them, they very wisely eased it, and once more the planing type of dinghy is being built, for as well as easing the weight rule, which would allow boats to plane, an additional rule was made governing the rise of floor. So while these dinghies might still, with advantage be 25 lb. lighter, the altered rules have made for far better boats in the class; and as there are only five of these steep-floored dinghies little harm has been done and a great deal of good by the building of them, for while they are faster to windward (two of the five were in last year's first six of the Prince of Wales' Cup and another two in the first six this year), there need only be a good reach on the course and the planing type will scuttle away from them.

This was one of those disputes between a designer and those directing the development of a class and we do not know what defence the Dinghy Committee may have been able to bring forward in support of the action they took. As an advocate of the planing dinghy, Uffa loathed weight—indeed, he loathed weight in any boat! If, as he says, he had been obliged to design a type of boat he disliked merely to comply with their weight rule, it is no wonder that he found this galling. It seems surprising that, once the planing principle had been discovered, anything should be done which might impede its development. Perhaps there were those who resented this revolutionary concept? However, it all happened a long time ago . . .

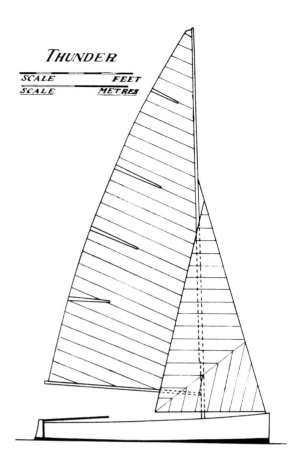

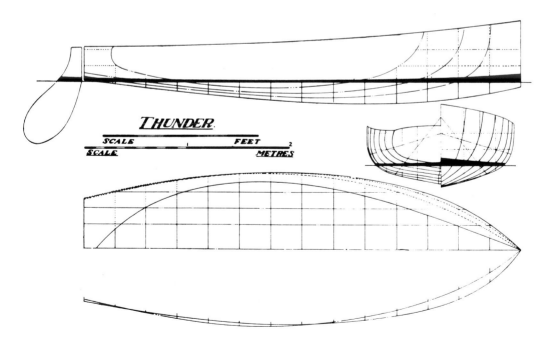

Thoughts on Yachts and Yachting

The book was written through the crisis of this most critical year of 1938, and this is the reason that there are no plans and very few photographs to illustrate the chapter describing the winning of the European Inland Waters' championship by a British crew; for the day on which I was writing to Germany for the plans of one of these boats, I received a lovely letter from a friend of mine in London with these words: "I do not think this is the right moment to write to Germany for these plans." That was on the Wednesday of the most critical week of the year, for even though the winter was coming on and winter wars have been unfashionable since Napoleon's retreat from Moscow, Hitler was rattling his sword in its scabbard and it looked as though a European war was inevitable that day.

Meanwhile as well as building racing yachts that would be a source of delight to their owners, we had to build a safe and secure dug-out to protect our workmen from impending air raids.

Once more we have in the cruising section craft to suit different tastes; but I have begun this section with some yarns and illustrations of some of the craft I have owned and sailed, and in so doing I have tried to explain just what each boat taught me, for every vessel and every cruise teaches us as long as we have the eyes to see. Therefore I hope that those who read the first chapter will, in sailing with me aboard these different boats, remember the lessons they taught me.

from *Introduction* to *Thoughts on Yachts and Yachting*

Dyarchy

Owner, Roger Pinckney
Designer, Laurent Giles
Builder, Truedesson

LOA 45 ft. 10 in. 13.97 m.
LWL 38 ft. 0 in. 11.58 m.
Beam 12 ft. 3 in. 3.73 m.
Draught 7 ft. 6 in. 2.29 m.
Displacement 24.2 tons 24,587 kilos.
Sail area 1,410 sq. ft. 131 sq. m.

When Roger Pinckney decided that his Bristol Channel pilot cutter *Dyarchy* should be replaced by a new vessel, he asked Laurent Giles to design her, and as Roger was an architect it was natural that he should have the type of vessel that he required in his mind, and so was of great help to the designer of the new *Dyarchy*.

We who love the sea and ships always see the virtues of every ship we sail in, and the virtues of the Bristol Channel pilot cutter are many. It is thus only natural that the new *Dyarchy* should be similar in type to her predecessor and namesake.

decks dry in a seaway, while aft the rudder is hung on her transom stern, a feature which simplifies any rudder problem that might arise throughout her life; ships have carried away their rudders through grounding and through getting stern way on in heavy weather, and when laid up for the winter in mud berths where the shore slopes to the water, rudders are subjected to severe strains, as the ship naturally tends to slide backwards to the water, and so puts her weight back on the rudder. But with such a boat as *Dyarchy* one imagines the rudder would be unshipped if laid up in a mud berth for the winter, as this is such a simple operation.

The sections show that she is a generous and well-rounded ship, a feature that makes for roominess below, and as this is blended with fair fore and aft lines *Dyarchy* sails along well in all weather conditions.

The fo'c'sle is fitted with lockers, while underneath the forward seat the WC is arranged. Immediately abaft this is the double-berthed forward cabin with seats and sideboards arranged in front of the berths, and it will be noted that the skylight is set athwartships over a bulkhead dividing the fo'c'sle from the fore cabin, so that the one skylight serves the purpose of two separate

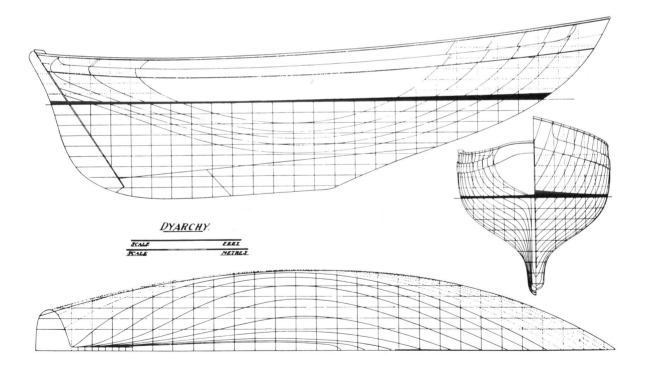

DYARCHY.

These pilot cutters were developed to stand up to the heavy seas and winds found on the lee side of the Atlantic, conditions which call for a strong, manly and seamanlike vessel, both in hull and rig.

Dyarchy closely resembles that type, as she has a moderate overhang forward, which tends to keep her

ones and saves deck space and an extra hole cut into the deck.

Abaft the fore cabin is the saloon, which is arranged in a most unusual way. In the two forward corners are circular armchairs, which are a continuation of the settees, while the two after corners have sideboards,

Dyarchy *was completed in 1939. She was still actively cruising in 1978 under the ownership of W. H. Batten, a flag officer of the Royal Cruising Club. He bought her from Roger Pinckney, so she has only ever had two owners.*

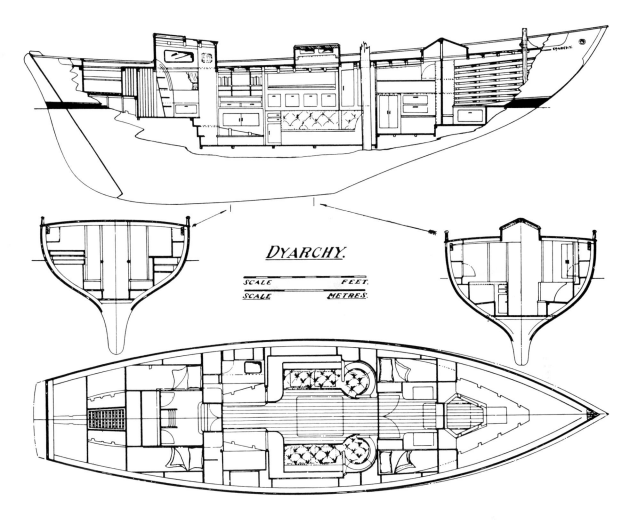

DYARCHY.

SCALE _____ FEET.

SCALE _____ METRES.

the settees extending under these sideboards in order to give full length for lying down or sleeping should they be required. Immediately aft and to port is the galley and pantry, while abreast to starboard is the chart room and table. We now ascend three stairs into the double-berthed after cabin with its small deck house to give full head room, and to form the companion way out over the wide bridge deck into the cockpit. The latter seems at first sight on the small side, but as it is self-bailing, the smaller the size the less water there is to be drained away in the event of a heavy sea coming aboard, for as the cockpit is so close to the after end of the vessel she is more likely to fill it with a sea over the stern than if she had a well-proportioned counter, but the weather would be very bad indeed and the vessel driven too hard when this would happen, for such a buoyant ship would lift and rise over most seas providing those on board gave her a chance.

Once in a square-sterned boat we were driving her far too hard when chasing away before a gale of wind, and she pulled a sea in over the stern, which, besides filling her self-bailing cockpit, filled her cabin up to the bunk level, but immediately we took sail off her and let her drive along at a speed to suit the seas, she showed no tendency at all to pull them in over the stern. So it would seem that the point to remember with short-sterned boats is that there is a limit to the speed at which they can be driven before a gale and steep breaking seas, and that this limit is reached earlier in square-sterned boats than in those with well-designed counters, which do not disturb the following sea so much and so tend to pull it aboard.

This is the way of the world, and all things have their advantages and disadvantages, and only the owners of vessels can decide what advantages they want and what they will endure to get them.

With her mast stepped so far aft, *Dyarchy*'s sail plan looks very seamanlike and workmanlike; it gives her an easily handled mainsail, and as the fore triangle is divided up by three headsails she is easy to work, for the smaller the largest sail is on any vessel the easier she is to work, and *Dyarchy*'s mainmast exactly divides the base of her total sail area in half. She is as easy to work as any cutter can be, and such a rig combines the ease of

DYARCHY.

handling of a schooner with the speed of the cutter rig.

The peak halyard, it will be noticed, is wire, as also is the throat, so fewer parts are needed, and these do not have to be set up every watch as rope halyards must always be because of their continual stretch, a feature which saves weight and windage aloft and work for those on board *Dyarchy*.

The worm roller reefing gear such as developed by the Bristol Channel pilot cutter is found on *Dyarchy*'s mainboom, which is stiff enough to stand sheeting at the outer end, and as this is plumb over the transom the main sheet lead is fair.

The forestay is set well abaft the stemhead, while the jib and jib topsail stays go to the bowsprit end. The bowsprit, steeved upwards to follow the sheer line of the boat, is pleasing to a seaman's eye, for so often the spar is set parallel to the water-level at rest, an unseamanlike practice, which has caused many a vessel to ship solid water in her jibs and so carry away her bowsprit. This is a source of danger, for the heavy spar then flogs and pounds at her bow while her crew have the dangerous task of trying to smother and gather in the mess.

Eric Hiscock it was, I believe, who said that in *Dyarchy* he learned to cruise "without fuss". I fancy she cradled a good many yachtsmen through the days of their sailing infancy. Her early spring cruise to the Channel Islands to be laid ashore for a scrub became almost an event in the yachting calendar. She was, above all, a comfortable ship and Roger Pinckney's mother continued cruising in her at a very advanced age.

Later, the upper section of *Dyarchy*'s mast was built out on its after side and formed into a groove to take the luff rope of the topsail. The topsail halyard passed over a sheave at the masthead, down the groove, and through the centre of a traveller, free to move up and down in the groove, but prevented from dropping out by a stop. The traveller centred the halyard and guided the head of the sail into the groove, where it pushed the traveller up ahead of it. Instead of a shackle securing the halyard to the head of the sail there was a cone-shaped screw fitting so that it would enter the groove easily. Other refinements would probably have been introduced into the gaff rig if people had not lost interest in it.

Dyarchy was the quintessence of the English cutter—one of the last of her line.

Sheila II

Owner, Paddy O'Keefe
Designer, Albert Strange
Builder, A. M. Dickie

LOA 31 ft. 6 in.
LWL 24 ft. 0 in.
Beam 8 ft. 6 in.
Draught 4 ft. 11 in.
Displacement 6·2 tons
Sail area 545 sq. ft.

Albert Strange, that fine artist and great designer, was one of the leading members of the Humber Yawl Club, and his name always conjures up pictures of the lovely little yawls he designed, which were so manly that they could be found cruising all round the British Isles. One still meets and hears of them on many different parts of the coast. *Sheila II* is at present stationed in the south-west of Ireland, for Paddy O'Keefe, her owner, sails and lives in that part of the world.

Built twenty-seven years ago, *Sheila II* is still in first-rate condition in spite of, or possibly because of, the fact that she has sailed thousands of miles along the western coasts of England, Ireland and Scotland, coasts which are exposed to the full force of the Atlantic wind and seas, for she has always had good owners, men who have not only been good seamen, but good ship's husbands, as they must be to sail on these exposed coasts, for the failure of any part of her gear might easily have led to her foundering on any one of the rocky headlands she has fought her way round.

Sheila has the moderate overhangs and the canoe stern so pleasing to the eye, and so characteristic of Albert Strange, while the sections, though being fast and easily driven, are such as to give that good floor space and accommodation which is so difficult to get, but which is so necessary in small boats.

Albert Strange designed so many of these small cruising yawls before he drew up the plans for *Sheila II* that it is difficult indeed to improve upon the arrangement and accommodation plans. The saloon in such a small boat can only be in the middle of the ship where the sections are fullest, and as men will always remain the same size, *Sheila*'s saloon is placed in the best possible position, and while minor details such as sideboards and such things can be added in a saloon, we could not improve upon *Sheila*'s saloon to-day.

Forward of this, through a sliding door, is the fo'c'sle with a folding cot. If this door swung it would take up space and be awkward, but as it is on the port side it can slide alongside the bulkhead and take up no room and be out of the way whether open or shut.

Abaft the saloon the galley is placed to starboard and lamp and oilskin lockers to port, while a WC is neatly fitted, so that it forms the bottom part of the companion way to the locker forming the bridge

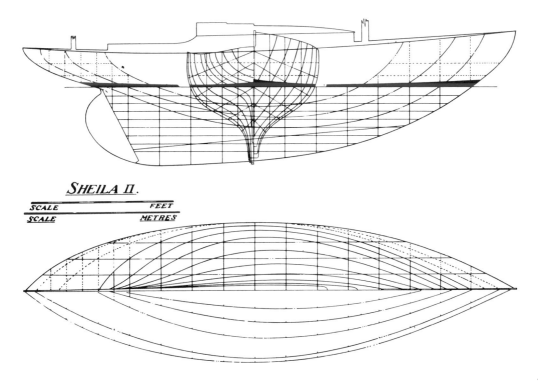

SHEILA II.

SCALE   FEET
SCALE   METRES

between the cabin and the water-tight cockpit. In this way the WC is isolated from the rest of the ship.

So many things have to be stowed and carried on small yachts that it is only after years of experience that the best place for each can be found, and though drawn just on thirty years ago this accommodation plan can still be of great interest to designers, builders and owners, for having designed so many successful cruisers of this size and type Albert Strange had

120 sq. ft., a mainsail with 283 sq. ft., a mizen of 72 sq. ft., and for catching the light airs aloft on calm days, a topsail with 72 sq. ft. in it.

Looking at her sail plan, we see that for normal weather her jib is set on a wooden roller, so is easily handled, but that for hard weather she sets a storm jib on her stemhead. The topsail may seem to entail a lot of work to our eyes to-day, but *Sheila* has no power other than that supplied by her crew on the end of a sweep;

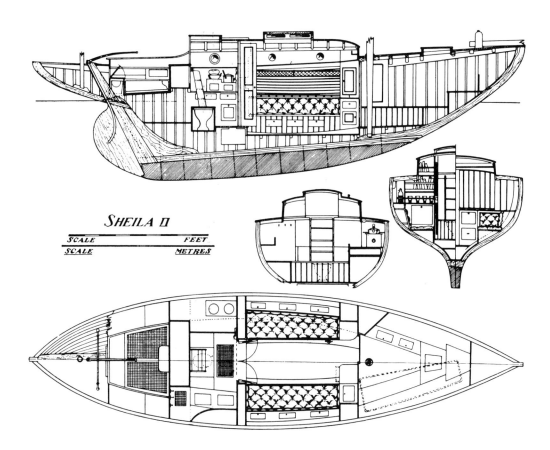

SHEILA II

SCALE ———— FEET
SCALE ———— METRES

worked out the best stowage place for everything. If we look at the sections, at the after end of the cabin, on the starboard side we see the blanket locker forming the after end of the starboard settee and also forming the shelf to take the glasses and the syphon of soda, while above this are bookshelves to take the ship's library. Albert Strange has designed a place for everything a cruising man requires on such a small vessel, so it is not to be wondered at that these little Humber yawls are such lovely little ships, and such a joy to their owners whether at sea or in harbour.

The sail plan is that developed by the seagoing members of the Club.

Sheila's total area of 545 sq. ft. is made up by a jib of

and the crutch shown on the cockpit coaming conjures up a picture of the crew sweating away at her "wooden topsail" that makes the bending and setting of her jackyard topsail seem easy and great fun, as indeed the setting of a jackyarder is. The ease and simplicity of the present-day Bermudian rig has robbed us of many pleasant moments setting sails, and though it might seem that the yards of this topsail would clutter up the deck, in fact they do not, for they stow up and down the main shrouds when not in use.

The setting of a gaff mainsail gives scope for quite a lot of skill. A good seaman could generally make any gaff mainsail set well, for, being bounded by four sides, he could set and adjust any one to perfect the whole.

SHEILA II.

Nowadays a mainsail is hauled out on a boom, and up a straight mast, and little can be done to help a bad sail; so it is throughout life, we gain in one direction and lose in another.

The mizen, being practically a gunter lug, is a step towards our present triangular sails, but even with this sail one had the fun of setting it to perfection, so although *Sheila*'s sail plan with its gaffs and jackyard topsail seems strange to our eyes, it still has much to recommend it, especially when we remember that most cruising is to leeward, and that a gaff sail is probably faster to leeward than the present-day Bermudian sail.

So because of all the pleasant memories of bygone days and people brought back by *Sheila II* I hope that future years will see her married to such men as Robert E. Groves, for whom she was designed and built and to Paddy O'Keefe, her present owner, good seamen and ship's husbands.

This boat later sailed to New Zealand—a protracted voyage of several year's duration described in the book, "Sheila in the Wind" by Adrian Hayter. Her sea-going ability was proved beyond doubt. She has the look of a real sea-boat, though deep-water voyaging was probably the last thing her designer had in mind. At one time it was possible to speak of, "an Albert Strange Yawl" and everyone knew instantly what was meant. They were a very distinct type.

I really must join issue with Uffa over the position of the WC. It seems to me to be located in the most ludicrous place possible and I think the designer deserved to be well and truly trodden on by someone descending in a hurry while he was sitting there. The two doors leading into the saloon seem to our eyes superfluous; but in those days people had a penchant for cutting their yachts up into separate compartments. One thing about those doors, though, sleepers on a night passage could be isolated from the cockpit conversation and the clatter in the galley of a "brew-up". But watch out for your fingers!

Sometimes the designs of these old boats (note the comment that this is not contemporary, but already twenty-seven years old) seem glaringly impractical. An example here is the helmsman's seat under the tiller: he could hardly sit on the sharp coaming.

Selina King

Owner, Arthur Ransome
Designer, Fred Shepherd
Builder, H. King & Sons

LOA 35 ft. 6 in. 10·82 m.
LWL 28 ft. 4 in. 8·64 m.
Beam 10 ft. o in. 3·05 m.
Draught 5 ft. o in. 1·52 m.
Displacement 10·25 tons 10,414 kilos.
Sail area 562 sq. ft. 52·21 sq. m.

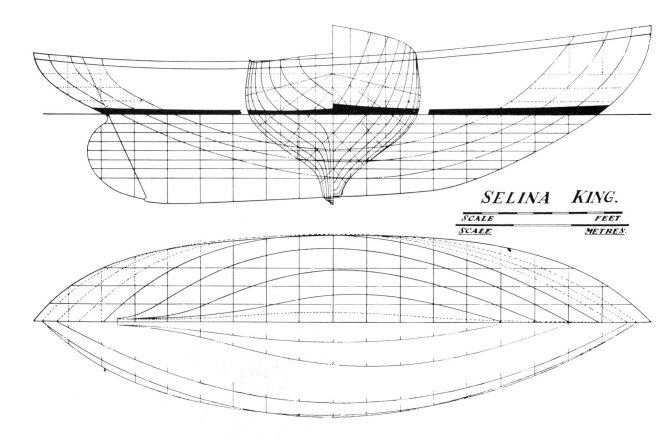

SELINA KING.

SCALE   FEET
SCALE   METRES.

"Well, I shall never build again." So wrote Arthur Ransome immediately after he had finished building his cruiser *Racundra* on the Baltic, but here we see that he has built once again, but this time more wisely, for *Selina King* was built on the shores of his own native land.

Nothing can be brought into this world without labour and pain, but that is soon lost sight of, and in its place comes the pleasure of seeing the thing we have created living its life; and it is because of this latter fact that the human race will continue, and owners will continue to build their own yachts.

We, who have known the writings of Arthur Ransome for many years, would expect him to go to Fred Shepherd for his designs, for Arthur Ransome is a cruising man, and Fred Shepherd has throughout his life been noted for his fine sturdy cruisers, and the wonderful accommodation he arranges in them, and so *Selina King* represents the thoughts of a great writer translated into plans, and then into a vessel by Fred Shepherd as the designer and H. King the builder.

With only 5 ft. o in. draught she is able to make almost any harbour she would wish to sail into, and her full generous body has made possible accommodation which is truly wonderful on this size vessel for there is no doubt that the well "V'd" sections above the water-line forward and aft make for a very comfortable boat in a seaway.

A Bermudian cutter rig has been chosen, and with the mast one third of the water-line length from its fore end this gives a snug mainsail with only $344\frac{1}{4}$ sq. ft., a sail that could be easily handled by one man under all conditions of wind and sea.

The mainboom is only 17 ft. 6 in. overall length, and this is fitted with a roller reefing gear, all of which enables those on board to take in or shake out a reef very easily and quickly.

It is always a problem in a cruising boat of this size whether to have double or single head sail rig. A racer this size will undoubtedly have a single headsail rig, but in a cruiser there are a great many other things to consider, as a cruiser is designed to stand all conditions of wind and sea. A single headsail would put heavier strains upon the mast and also make the handling more difficult, whereas with the double headsail rig, things are much easier, for with a close reefed mainsail the jib could be taken in and stowed below, for the vessel would then be perfectly balanced with a staysail and close reefed mainsail only, and any changes in headsails could be easily made, for one sail is run up in the lee of the other, sheeted home and then the other one stowed, so though the luffs of these two sails are so close together (only 2 ft. 6 in. separates them) there is much to recommend them for a cruising vessel, especially when we bear in mind the fact that the forestay can easily be taken into the mast and cleared out of the way when the large genoa is being used in fine weather.

The area of the genoa, 365 sq. ft., is greater than that of the mainsail, and brings home to us the fact that such sails are most seamanlike, for they enable the sail area

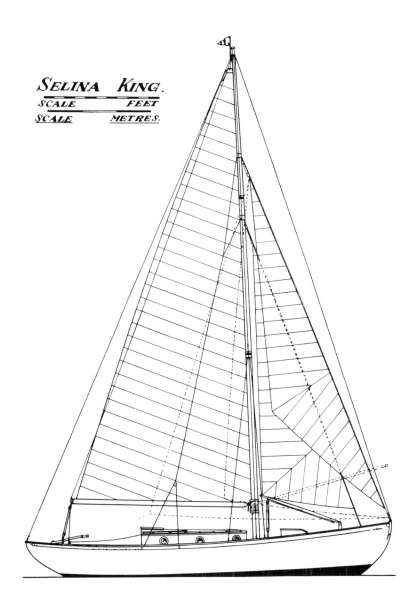

SELINA KING.
SCALE   FEET
SCALE   METRES.

of a cruiser to be increased enormously in light weather without any increase in spars, and the use of such sails will save us and yachtsmen of the future from the over sparred cruisers we had fifty years ago, so the sail plan gives us food for thought.

With her long iron keel she can take the ground and not fear any damage through rough bottom or straining, for such a keel forms a strong girder, and so strengthens as well as protecting her from harm.

The saloon has two full length settee berths, a little stove and coal locker being at the fore end of the starboard berth, while abaft it is the galley and plate rack, while there is a writing and chart table and oilskin locker at the after end of the port berth, and the hinged top of the bridge deck gives access to the engine which is underneath it. Fuel tanks are arranged under the side seats of the self-bailing cockpit, and as the head lining runs out to the outer side of the cockpit coaming, any waste fuel and fumes are bailed overboard automatically.

Practically every cruiser to-day has an engine, and the engine chosen is a Morris Cadet Marine with reduction gear. This 5–12 h.p. engine drives her along at a steady 6 knots, enabling her owner to be sure of making port when the wind falls away to a calm.

There is no doubt that *Selina King* is a fine little cruiser, which can either be sailed single handed or with three on board, and there is no doubt she will make many prosperous voyages, and I hope and believe that future years will see us enjoying a book by her owner on the sojourning of *Selina King*.

Those who have found Arthur Ransome's books charming may be interested in the yacht he had built for himself. She seems to have been a pretty average sort of boat for that time. Uffa earnestly mulls over the problem of the fore triangle and it is difficult to avoid being smug in our knowledge that all this was subsequently resolved by the standard Bermudian sloop rig. The foredeck must have been very cluttered. I like the toilet arrangements up forward. Yachting people of today may find the idea of removing the wash-basin from its cut-out hole and emptying it into the WC primitive; but it did avoid the additional plumbing of a waste-pipe. I am all for simplicity in a boat. Every added complication is something else to go wrong. We would expect more berths on an overall length of 35 ft. 6 ins.; but that was their style, they liked some space to move around in—and with building costs what they were then, why not?

Of *Uffa Fox's Second Book*, Arthur Ransome had already said in a review for the *Manchester Guardian*: "He never flags for a moment. Nor can his readers. Sailor, boat builder, designer and admirable writer. Go it, Uffa! And if, as you promised, you are going to make a habit of it, and give us a new book every year, you provide a new motive for longevity."

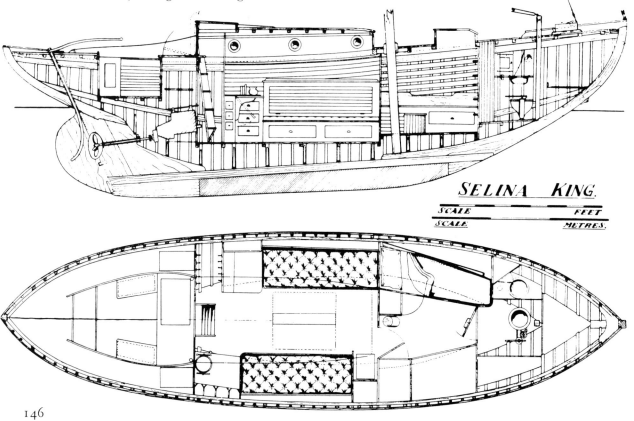

SELINA KING.

SCALE   FEET
SCALE   METRES.

Askoy

Owner, Hugo Van Kuyck
Designer, Hugo Van Kuyck
Builder, John Cockerill

LOA 55 ft. 0 in. 16·76 m.
LWL 45 ft. 11 in. 14 m.
Beam 14 ft. 6 in. 4·42 m.
Draught 7 ft. 8 in. 2·34 m.
Displacement 36·6 tons 37·84 kilos.
Sail area 1,604 sq. ft. 148·98 sq. m.

A long time ago Hugo Van Kuyck told me of his dream to sail round the world, and his idea and method of doing this was so good that I was full of admiration for it.

Most of us have to work in this life, hence we find that most cruising men have their yachts out for a few months and enjoy them during that time, but for the rest of the year they are laid up as the owners cannot spare the time to sail in them. Hugo Van Kuyck's idea was that, when the vessel was laid up, it did not matter a great deal in what country the operation was performed; and as he could get away for a month or so every year, he decided to design and build his ocean cruiser to take him round the world, and to spend so much of each year sailing her so far round, returning home to work and then rejoining his ship again later on to continue his circumnavigation. In this way he would realise his ambition of sailing round the world during his normal holidays, in direct contradiction to the accepted idea that this very long voyage can only be undertaken by those with unlimited time at their disposal. And as Van Kuyck is looked upon in Antwerp as a leading architect and civil engineer, he has little time for sailing. Looking at *Askoy*'s lines, we see she is designed to be a comfortable ship at sea with a great deal of room on board, and one that will sail steadily before the Trades and following winds, which are virtues in an ocean cruiser; and though some might doubt her ability to go to windward, there are not many of us who wish to go to windward across oceans, as that is the hard way. We who have sailed across oceans have always made a practice of getting on the best leg when the wind has come ahead, and sailing a point or so free of close hauled, letting our vessel go through the water fairly easily until the wind once more enables us to lay our course. When we bear this in mind and remember the extra accommodation afforded by the deep fore foot, we realise that *Askoy* makes a very fine ocean cruiser indeed.

To drive this hull, a topsail schooner rig was chosen, for though some might call her a staysail schooner, as all the fore and aft sails forward of the mainmast are staysails, she is actually a topsail schooner with a main

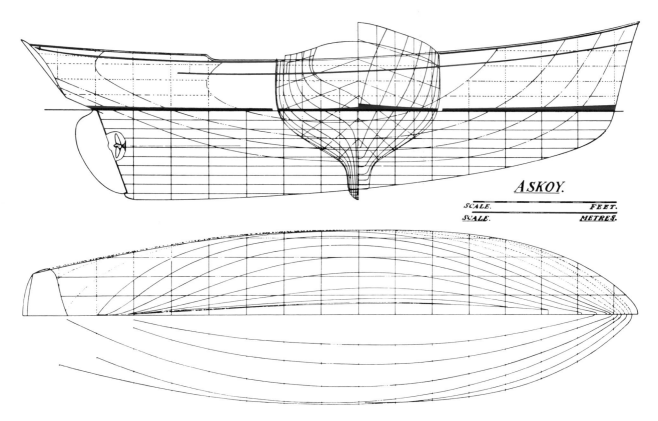

ASKOY.

SCALE.   FEET.
SCALE.   METRES.

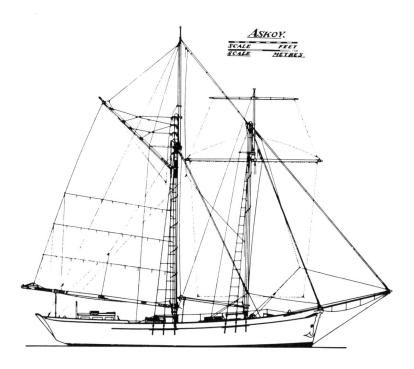

ASKOY.
SCALE   FEET.
SCALE   METRES.

and main topmast staysail instead of the normal foresail and fore topsail; and this combination of the old and new is a pleasing one, as for close hauled work one has the advantages of well setting staysails forward of the mainmast, while for running there is the topsail and square sail to lift and drive her along as she chases away before the wind.

It will be noticed she is fitted with fidded topmasts, and should either of these carry away she would still be quite happy though she might not sight another vessel for a month. This is an important point for ocean cruisers; they really should not be designed with rigs such as we use in our racing craft round the coasts, for with the racing rigs the failure of any one part or shroud generally causes the whole to collapse and fall down round our ears. *Askoy* has a rig to match her hull, for both give one a sense of security at sea.

Her deck plan reminds us of a big ship and big ship's practice, as at the stem head there are gratings and these are also to be found at the after end of the poop deck, the latter giving head room in the after cabin. The inner end of the bowsprit is anchored by sturdy bits, and abreast these on either side are two catheads for getting the anchors aboard. These also take the bowsprit shrouds, which are set up, like the main shrouds of the ship, by deadeyes and lanyards, the main shrouds coming down to channels which stand well out from the ship's side, a feature that gives greater spread to the rigging and at the same time more room on the deck, as the shrouds do not cut across the shoulders of those aboard as they walk past.

These various points and *Askoy*'s rig are good features in a vessel bound round the globe, for lanyards, deadeyes, solid spars, etc., can be found and rigged in almost any part of the world, whereas rigging screws and fancy gadgets are almost impossible to come by once a vessel is off the beaten track, and the fun of travelling round the world is to get off this.

No vessel has ever yet been ready in time and so *Askoy* started four months later than expected on her voyage round the world; her stores, amounting to tons of oil, water, gear, sails, instruments and arms, had to be stowed in the winter months by her cheerful crew of four, Rudi Schonberg, the mate; Carl de Grijze, botanist, and A.B.; Oscar Paar, engineer; Robert Francis, cook; the two last ones cadets of the Belgian training ship *Mercator*, but in the end *Askoy* was ready and she left Antwerp on January 16, 1938, on her long voyage. She called at Dover, Falmouth, Porto and Lisbon, from where the big adventure started, and in twenty-nine days *Askoy* had reached Martinique in the West Indies, with a one day stop at Madeira between.

This twenty-nine day voyage was an uneventful passage except that in latitude 19° north she ran into a south-west area which lasted five days. All on board were excited as they saw their first Portuguese men-of-war, their first bonitos, their first whales and their first flying fishes (we all are), and were highly delighted with their ship, her square rig and with the crusty bread baked by the cook throughout the voyage.

It is surprising how quickly the weeks pass at sea with a cheerful, willing crew aboard, and as this was in

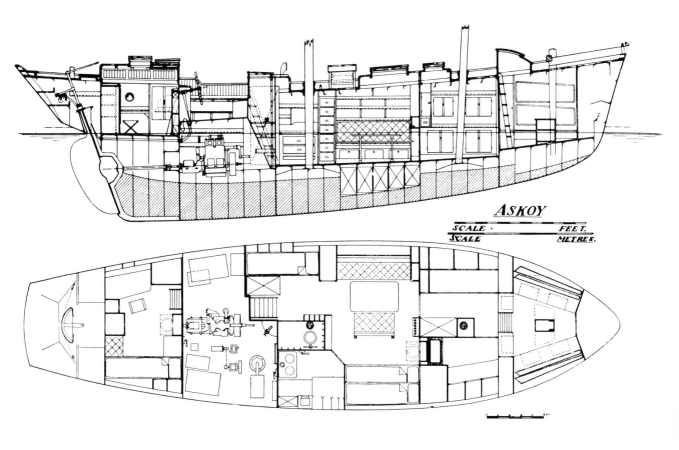

ASKOY

SCALE · FEET.
SCALE METRES.

the nature of a trial cruise *Askoy* was full of new and pleasant surprises for all on board by her seaworthiness and kindly motion in a sea.

At Martinique Hugo Van Kuyck had to leave his ship to fly to the States as he had to lecture on Architecture to the Yale University in New Haven, after which he returned to Antwerp to work once more at his job of designing yachts and houses, but not for long, as the mate took *Askoy* on to Panama where two American scientists are to join the expedition and where he will join her again in February ready to continue her way on to Tahiti, New Guinea, Japan, the Philippines and the Dutch Indies.

A good many round-the-world voyages have been marred by anxiety over haphazard finances—a few guineas wrested from the editor of a magazine for an article, some casual chartering, a spell working on shore. Hugo Van Kuyck seems to have arranged things rather better than that, planning to accomplish his voyage in stages,

returning between whiles to earn some more money and retain his professional connections.

Uffa queries *Askoy*'s ability to go to windward, and so do I—with that tubby hull and the windage of all the spars aloft? I cannot help thinking she would have done better under an orthodox small boat rig; but none can deny she has a fine romantic look about her, a ship to search for buried treasure—doubloons and pieces of eight. And what if the only treasure is the memory of tall palms leaning over a tropical lagoon, or the ship heeling to a brisk North East Trade? Are not such memories also a treasure? No government can claim them as treasure trove, nor any jugglery of international financiers debase their value. Even in crabbed old age, amid the confinement brought on by loss of mobility, they will offer the consoling thought that life was not always so.

Actually, re-reading Uffa's notes, I find there was a botanist among the crew and provision for a dark-room and a laboratory in the accommodation lay-out, so it looks as though some kind of scientific research was intended; but all this is usually only an excuse to go, anyway, and see the world.

Long Distance Racing, 1938

Every year sees an increase in the number of Long Distance Races, and an increase in the number of ships and men taking part. Twelve years ago we had only one such race (the Fastnet); there were some thirty races in the summer of 1938. A glance at the chart at the head of this chapter, on which many of the courses are shown, reveals the fact that we in the British Isles are fortunate in having so many countries, Norway, Sweden, Germany, Holland and France, within striking distance, thus enabling us to lay out courses which are full of interest and fun, as without being long and tedious, they take us to another country where the language and customs are different. And though the longest race, from Dover to Kristiansand, is only 488 miles in length, on arriving one has all the feeling of having travelled thousands of miles and finding a new country and people. This is one of the reasons for the increasing popularity of the races under the Royal Ocean Racing Club's Rules. Another reason is that, although the older generation tends to look down upon the present, yachting today has become a more manly sport, for now long voyages are made in very small yachts by a greater number of people, whereas in the past only a few made long voyages, and these generally in large comfortable vessels. By the present generation I mean those who are sailing today, from the young men of eighty to the old men of sixteen and eighteen, as one and all meet on a level footing when they step aboard their vessels' deck to take part in these races.

THE CHANNEL RACE

Years ago the Fastnet race was open to quite small boats, but after one or two severe heavy weather races it was decided to split the fleet into two groups, so that only vessels of 35 ft. and over could take part in the Fastnet, a race of 200 miles in length being arranged for the smaller class. By this reasoning it seems a little unfair that the larger craft should race round the Channel course, thus taking away some of the glory from the smaller boats, who look upon the Channel race as their championship. So though the large class as usual sailed round this course, the race is essentially the smaller class championship race.

There were twenty-seven starters, and *Cynthia* led round the course, and so won the Forsyth Cup for the first boat home. *Wanda*, however, was the winner of the Channel Cup.

A smart fair breeze made short miles of the first leg to the *Owers* and to Beachy Head, but after this the wind fell away, and, though it freshened a bit through the night, remained so light and variable that the race as a whole developed into a slow and tedious struggle with the constant changing of light sails. The run from Beachy Head to the *Royal Sovereign* took a long time, but once round all the racers stood across the weather-going tide on the starboard tack to take every advantage from it.

The breeze freshened a little away to the *Havre Lightship*, but over on the French coast very light airs and calms were experienced. *Oenone* rounded the *Havre Lightship* first, with *Cynthia* hard on her heels, but for the next ten hours or so the variable airs and calms gave those on board a great deal of work. The wind came after a while strong enough to enable the racers to finish, but the slow going had helped smaller vessels, as one would expect, for with the time on time handicap the smaller craft get a longer handicap for light slow races, and often under these conditions a small boat is as fast as a larger one, for, brought down to its lowest level, when the wind is so light that both are becalmed, both are going the same speed, which is nil, but all the while they are becalmed the smaller boat is getting a longer handicap.

Evenlode led the large class home, though the same length water-line *Maid of Malham* received enough time under the Royal Ocean Racing Club's rating to bring her into first place for the large class.

There was a Royal Ocean Racing Club Cup for the club whose yachts came out top for points throughout the whole season in their events, and the Royal Naval Sailing Association won this with a long lead, as they had a 31-point lead from the next, the Royal Thames Yacht Club, while the R.N.S.A.'s *Maid of Malham* won the Trenchemer Cup, which is given to the ocean racer scoring the most points.

OPEN CLASSES—*Maid of Malham*, 121; *Phryna*, 80.5; *Ortac*, 80; *Westwind*, 72; *Erivale*, 71; *Firebird*, 55; *Aile Noire*, 44.

SMALL CLASS—*Prelude*, 49; *Inverie*, 42; *Wanda*, 39; *Allegro*, 35; *Droleen*, 35.

FAST CRUISERS—*Macnab*, 71; *Tai-mo-shan*, 53; *Banba*, 51; *Ilex*, 44.5.

'B' CRUISERS—*Wanadis*, 38; *Aideen*, 31; *Valiant*, 26.5.

There were a great many more events, and so large is the number of people interested in long distance racing that one wonders if it would not be a good idea to hold the Fastnet as an annual instead of a biennial event, and so leave the small class their championship race free of the bigger class, the two races starting at the end of Cowes Week. For with Cowes Week filled with gentle handicap racing and fun on shore, it is possible to collect a great many more racers from France, Germany, Holland, Denmark, Norway and Sweden, etc., and they would enjoy a week of easy yachting before taking part in the Channel and Fastnet races, which would be all the more enjoyable, as they would make such a contrast.

SIX-METRES
Circe

Owner, John H. Thom
Designer, Donald Boyd
Builder, Alex. Robertson & Son Ltd.

LOA 38 ft. 6 in. 11·734 m.
LWL 23 ft. 6 in. 7·162 m.
Beam 6 ft. 1 in. 1·854 m.
Draught 5 ft. 6 in. 1·676 m.
Displacement 4·018 tons 4,082 kilos.
Sail area 452·5 sq. ft. 42·03 sq. m.

It gives me a great deal of joy and pleasure to head this chapter with *Circe*. In the first place her designer, Donald Boyd, has for years been producing lovely vessels of all types, and in *Circe* he has produced a "six" to delight a seaman's heart, for *Circe* loves hard winds and weather. Moreover, she was built by Alexander Robertson & Son of Sandbank, and as I am the proud owner of the original gig built by them for the famous old *Britannia* over forty years ago, I know how well and truly Robertson of Sandbank build, for even to-day the build of that gig delights my heart.

ference put limitations on the beam of the different classes: no 6-metre could have less than 6-ft. beam, no 8-metre less than 8-ft. beam, no 10-metre less than 9·9-ft. beam, and no 12-metre less than 11·8-ft. beam without a heavy penalty, for all these classes had tended to become narrower, wet and uninspiring boats with little room inside. It is encouraging to see that *Circe* with her 6 ft. 1 in. beam is capable of beating the crack 6-metre *Goose* in hard weather, and there is no doubt that *Circe*'s beam helped her to stand up to the hard winds experienced in the races for the Seawanhaka Cup on Long Island Sound in September 1938.

The fore and aft lines are very pleasing to the eye, while the sections showing her powerful bilges are also a delight to look upon, so that when we look at Donald Boyd's interpretation of the international rule we feel that in spite of all the criticism levelled at it by all of us the rule is good, in that fine little vessels that are most successful can be designed to the rule.

The construction plan shows that the bottom of her lead keel is practically parallel to the water-line, so that every advantage is taken of the draught limit put on by the rule and the removal a year or so ago of the midship girth penalty. This long low lead keel added to her beam and firm bilges, in combination with her clean fore and aft lines, is the reason that *Circe* was successful

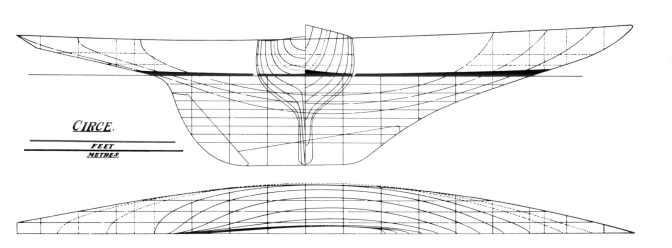

CIRCE.

FEET
METRES.

Then her owner and helmsman, John H. Thom, has for years been looked upon as one of our best helmsmen, so *Circe* has the combination of the three things needed for a successful boat, a wonderful designer, first class builder and a crack helmsman as owner.

Twenty-three and a half feet seems to be the right length water-line for a 6-metre, as for some years now all the crack "sixes" have been around this length, so one would expect *Circe* to be of this length water-line.

Last autumn the International Yacht Racing Con-

in bringing back to British waters the Seawanhaka Cup, for in those races she met the hard winds she loves and revels in.

A close study of *Circe*'s construction plan shows that she is well and truly built, for she has an inner diagonal skin of mahogany of $\frac{5}{32}$ in. in thickness, while her outer fore and aft mahogany skin is $\frac{15}{32}$ in. thick. Everywhere every detail has been carefully thought out and developed, and she is a craft that, while designed for racing and a successful racer, will give many years of sport and pleasure when her racing career is over.

Circe beating in Cowes Roads with Goose *just ahead.*

The sail plan shows she has a base of 10 ft. 6 in. to her fore-triangle, while her main boom is 16·13 ft. in length. Her jib and mainsail, as one would expect, goes up to the maximum height allowed by the rule.

The 452·55 sq. ft. allowed her by the rule is made up by the main sail of 309·85 sq. ft. and a fore-triangle of 142·70 sq. ft., a proportion of mainsail to fore-triangle that seems particularly suited to *Circe* with her hard weather ability, and the more we study the more we understand and appreciate the thought and work put into *Circe* by her designer and builder.

The 6-metres enjoyed a good season's sport on the

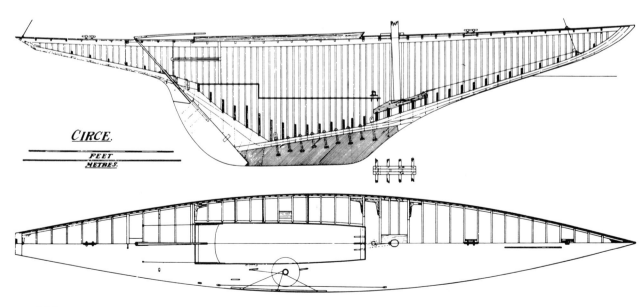

CIRCE.

FEET
METRES.

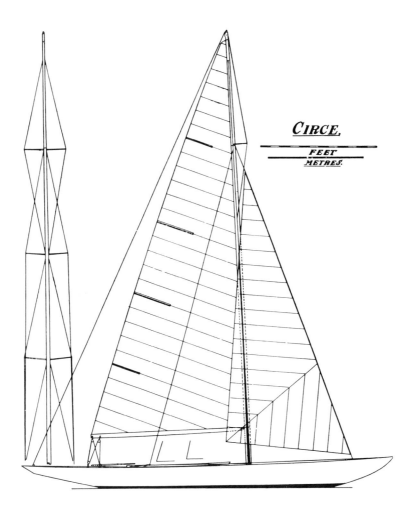

CIRCE.

FEET
METRES.

Clyde, on the Solent and at Burnham, the Burnham "sixes" visiting the Solent for Cowes Week, which takes the first week of August, and the Solent "sixes" returning this visit by racing on the Crouch during Burnham Week, which generally takes the first week of September.

However, the three important championships for the 6-metre class were held over in America, where as always the 6-metre contests were held in Oyster Bay.

When Uffa wrote about *Circe*, the six-metres had the niche of being the "in" racing class, in a closely parallel way to the "Ton Cup" boats of today. The "latest six" was eagerly awaited as being the ultimate racing boat to date. The class raced regularly in many parts of Europe and had spread to Long Island Sound and parts of the eastern United States owing to the British-America Cup put up by the Seawanhaka Corin-

thian Yacht Club. *Goose* which he mentions, being beaten on one occasion by *Circe*, is today (1978) still racing at Seattle (after several conversions by her designers, Sparkman and Stephens). However, Seattle is the only place in the world that now sees six-metres racing regularly. It is ironic that these boats created by the IYRU in 1907 and which the North American Yacht Racing Union (as it then was) wanted nothing to do with until 1921, should now only exist in the USA.

Circe's designer, David Boyd, earned a high reputation from his six metres, but this was subsequently shattered when in 1958, he designed the British challenger for the America's Cup, the 12-metre *Sceptre*, which was crushingly defeated by *Columbia*, designed by his pre-war rival Olin J. Stephens. Both Stephens and Uffa considered the metre boats a good basis as fast sea going boats. Uffa sailed the six, *Lintie*, the 152 miles from Cowes to Burnham-on-Crouch in 21¾ hours, while Olin's *Dorade* was metre boat hull form adapted to ocean racing.

Craft I Have Owned and Sailed

There was a section in the book on Uffa's own previous craft and some of his escapades in others. Eighteen boats were mentioned in this way, starting with a 16 ft. sailing canoe, in which he sailed round the Isle of Wight at night, after a dance! The eighteenth was *Brynhild* (page 83). Among them were the following two.

Bonito II

Bonito II was my next boat, designed by Linton Hope to the 18 ft. linear rating rule. She was slim and swift, but had very low freeboard and a short keel with an independent rudder back beyond this, shaped like a duck's foot.

In *Bonito* I raced and cruised for several years, and she taught me that a short-keeled boat with overhangs would steer herself and be easy on the helm and be a very able sea boat, in contradiction to most people, who were convinced that exactly the opposite was true; for in a seaway the reserve buoyancy in her overhangs fore and aft gave her fore and aft stability, and the length of 26 ft. instead of 18 ft. as *Bonito* was on the water-line.

One cruiser race in particular comes back to me. Our course was taking us round the South Bramble buoy, and as we made towards this the light went out of the sky, and though it should have been broad daylight every light buoy in the Solent started to shine, so dark did it become. Then for want of a better word a tornado struck us, and though *Bonito* was hove right down, with her roller reefing gear I was able to reef away until the jaws of the gaff (she was a gunter lug)

were down on the main boom, and as I had already furled her roller head sail she was now snug and we continued our way round the course, whereas all the proper cruisers without reefing gear had to stow their mainsails entirely and were then unmanageable.

This tornado only lasted some ten minutes, and its path was only about 200 yards wide. After it had gone it rained heavily, and the wind dropped almost to nothing, so I was able to put full sail up again and complete the course, the only boat of the fleet able to do so, as the rest had blown away so far to leeward that when they re-set their sails they were unable to fight their way back to Cowes over the tide. Ever since that race I have always contended that every racer should be equipped so that she is able to reef and unreef and make changes in her sail area so that she can contend with every type of wind from calm to a heavy gale, as only then is she sure of completing the course.

Always when sailing *Bonito II* I felt grateful to Linton Hope, that past master of light displacement boats, for designing such a lovely though delicate little hull that was a source of delight in all weathers.

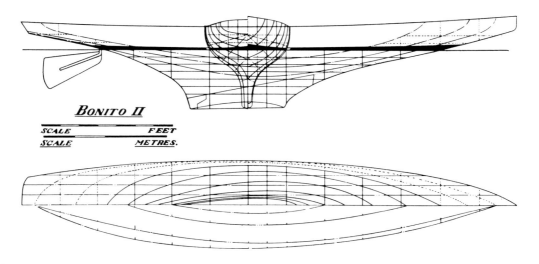

BONITO II

SCALE   FEET
SCALE   METRES.

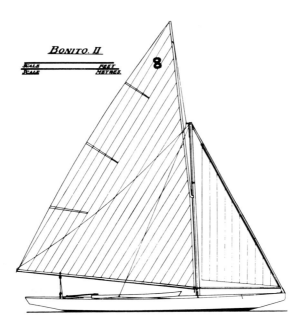

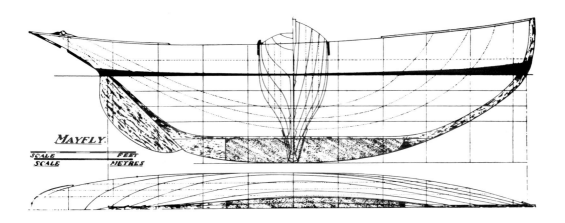

Mayfly (La Mascotte)

This cutter was an exact replica of the old successful plank on edge. *La Mascotte* was built by the Earl of Albemarle on his estate in Norfolk, and is such an interesting craft that, though I did not own her, an account of her run from Brightlingsea to Cowes seems to fit into this chapter.

To begin with, a great deal of her timber was walnut, grown on the estate of the Earl, and then the fact that an exact replica of one of the old narrow racing cutters was to be equipped with the Bermudian rig made her such an interesting craft, that I jumped for joy when her owner and builder gave me the chance of sailing her down to Cowes.

A friend and myself joined her at Brightlingsea, and we left in the early morning in a fairly strong northerly breeze. With full sail we were soon out amongst the sandbanks of the Thames Estuary, with *Mayfly* travelling at her highest speed, at which she pulled up a quarter wave astern which roared like an express train the whole time. It was some time before I grew used to this, and I kept looking at the chart to be sure I was crossing the different sands with enough water under me. For we all know in shallow water when a vessel starts to smell the bottom she pulls up a huge quarter wave astern. However, we did not touch the bottom as we sped along through the Barrow Deep, the

Fishermen's Gap, and the Edinburgh Channel on our way to the North Foreland.

We made very short miles of it down inside the Goodwins, through the Gull Channel and round the South Foreland. Here we brought the wind almost abeam, and our vessel now took up quite an alarming angle of heel, so much so that it was most uncomfortable below, for she was so narrow and deep that when at rest a man could stand upright in her cabin with his hands upon his hips and his elbows touching either side of the cabin, so she had a great deal of headroom but no footroom, but now this was all changed, for she was down on her beam ends and had a lot of footroom but absolutely no headroom at all. Still for all this she rushed along the south coast, and as we roared by the *Royal Sovereign*, chaps on board who knew me shouted out 'What ship, Uffa?' to which I replied 'Hardship!' for here we were laid out flat with the sea sweeping right over us, and though our speed was exhilarating it was most uncomfortable, and all we could get to eat was the hard tack we had on board.

Away we came down Channel, past the *Owers* where we had to steer up on a north-westerly course for the waters inside the Wight, and whereas before we had thought our vessel was laid out flat, she now showed us how little we knew of her. She lay over to such a degree that the lead keel was visible practically the whole time in the hollow between her bow and quarter wave on the weather side, and she carried so much lee helm that though fitted with a wishbone tiller the whole of my arm was in solid water as she ploughed her way up past the Nab and Warner to the Forts, where we were once more able to lay her off the wind a bit and let her come more upright. For all this angle of heel she was still streaking along and it seemed it did not matter at what angle this narrow hull sailed, for as long as she was driven hard she would go at her top speed, and we really enjoyed the way in which she soaked to windward from the *Owers* to the No-man fort (soaked is the proper word, for the two of us on board were wringing, while the vessel herself was soaking wet as one would expect, she was more like a submarine than a sailing boat when driven so hard to windward).

With the light getting stronger we really enjoyed the last reach inside the Wight to Cowes. An exact copy of an old three-tonner had sailed the 200 miles from Brightlingsea into Cowes harbour in 23 hours, which gave her an average speed of 8 knots for the whole way.

From *Mayfly* I got a clear view of the sport given to the owners of the narrow hulls that were successful under the old tonnage rule in 1880, and realised that, though we of this age condemn these hulls of fifty years ago, nevertheless they were capable of being driven at high speeds on all points of sailing no matter at what angle they were sailed.

She taught me, too, that for comfort at sea one should have a vessel that sails fairly upright, as to be at a heavy list always makes sailing into a hardship rather than into a pleasure. All cruisers should be designed to sail as upright as the righteous.

Thunder and Lightning

Owners, Peter Scott and J. K. Winter
Designer, Uffa Fox
Builder, Uffa Fox

LOA 13 ft. 11¾ in.
LWL 13 ft. 9 in
Beam 4 ft. 8¼ in.
Draught 8¼ in. and 5 ft. 6 in.
Displacement 800 lbs.
Sail area 125 sq. ft.

No matter how large or small a vessel, she always takes longer to build than the builders anticipate. This is due to a great many causes, one being the difficulty of getting material in time, for the building of a ship is one of the largest assembly jobs in this world, and if it is a big ship thousands of different firms are called in and each plays its part in building up the whole. Even on such a small boat as a 14-footer, it is surprising the number of different trades which contribute towards it. There are timber merchants, sawyers, wire rope makers, rope makers, cotton manufacturers, sail makers, makers of rigging screws, foundry workers, various engineering firms, the nail and screw manufacturers, right down to the little-known gold-beaters of London who beat out the gold leaf with which her name is put on. All of these are outside the control of the firm building the vessel, and delay caused through any one of these various trades causes a delay in the building of the dinghy.

Then, too, we also have to remember that the building of a 14-footer rests entirely on a skilful hand guided by a craftsman's brain, and this human element is sometimes ill, sometimes has family affairs to straighten up, for which time off is needed, and practically every job done by hand takes longer than estimated. *Thunder and Lightning* was no exception to the general rule that vessels are most difficult things to produce on time, for early in 1938 there was a great deal of illness amongst my workmen, which put all our programme back, then because the country was re-arming materials were not only expensive but difficult to obtain, so as usual we only just completed *Thunder and Lightning* in time for her first race, and right until the last moment it was doubtful if she would be ready.

She had been completed and taken into the paint shop for her final coats of varnish and name, so on the morning of the race we had to step the mast, fit toe straps, shackles, fairleads and the hundred and one jobs that cannot be done until after a boat is finally varnished; and in order to do this we had no less than half a dozen chaps collecting and fitting the final pieces of the puzzle.

Our yard is only a four-minute sail from the Island Sailing Club's starting line, so that at the ten-minute gun *Thunder and Lightning* still sat on the trestles; her jib was hoisted and she would soon be off; meanwhile she sat. Then she was launched, so that when the five-minute gun went she was 15 yards away from the slip on the way to the starting line, and so, as long as the breeze held, we knew she would be there in time, and as she sailed round to the start we, who had sweated so much that morning, replaced this with beer.

Thunder and Lightning had been designed for John Winter and Peter Scott, and as these two had both won the Prince of Wales' Cup in previous years, it was not surprising that she won this, her first race, and as in less than a week's time she also won the Prince of Wales' Cup race at Falmouth, she may fittingly illustrate our 14-ft. chapter.

Her lines are very similar to those of *Thunder,* in

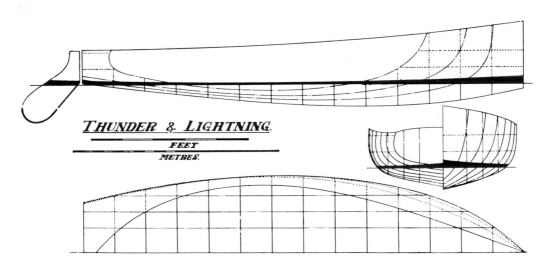

THUNDER & LIGHTNING.
FEET
METRES.

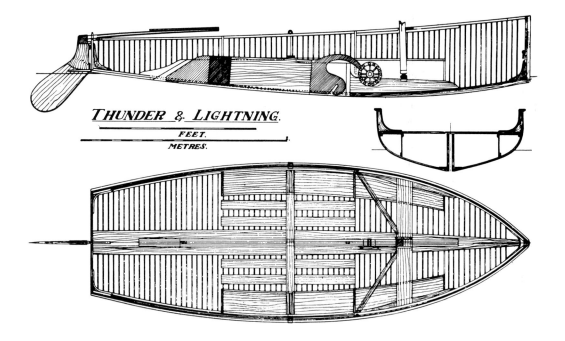

THUNDER & LIGHTNING.

FEET.

METRES.

which Peter won the Prince of Wales' Cup race last year, excepting that she is finer forward. Her arrangement, too, is very like *Thunder*'s, the most noticeable difference being a small rudder, and a centreboard swung on a pin instead of being suspended on rollers. Once again Peter continued his side tanks forward and did away with the bow tank, a good feature in normal weather, but bad in really hard weather, when the water surges forward as the dinghy rushes down the face of the sea, for then the normal bow tank prevents the water surging into the bow.

Then, too, in *Thunder and Lightning* we made the longer keel case and dropkeel, as we were not convinced that the maximum length of plate had been arrived at. This gave her a draught of 5 ft. 6 in., greater than the 6-metres.

The track taking the jib sheet slides was carried right away aft to the transom; but though there is no tax on the extremely large jibs on 14-footers, they have never yet really paid, for while they pull the boat along in the lightest of airs, the breeze has only to freshen the least bit for these large jibs to do more harm than good, and while the crew is changing them over the dinghy loses more than she has gained through their use. It would seem that the advantage of these large sails in 14-footers is a matter of luck, for if they have to be changed more is lost than gained by them, due to the fact that a sensitive boat like a 14-footer slows up during all sail changing, and this is not surprising when we remember that one man's weight is equal to half the weight of the boat complete with all her gear, and that any movement on his part upsets the boat to a very large extent. However, unless these things are tried and

tried again we should never progress, and in time I feel sure that a large jib will be made that is successful, not only because of its shape, but because the technique of changing it to the smaller in the event of wind will have been perfected. In one way and another, though *Thunder and Lightning* does not appear to differ greatly from Peter's *Thunder* of last year, there are many differences and refinements in her, and she represents the very latest development of the International 14-footer in Great Britain.

The Ranelagh Sailing Club at Putney arranges a winter programme over part of the Oxford and Cambridge Boat Race course, and so International 14-footers have continuous racing throughout the year, and there is really no beginning or ending to the season. Generally the summer season is reckoned to begin with the opening Regatta of the Island Sailing Club two weeks before Easter every year, as at this Regatta the new boats appear for the first time.

March 19 is early for Solent racing in open boats, but this year we once more had perfect weather for the mannequin parade of 14-footers, as there was a fresh south-westerly wind with warm sunshine. In the morning race *Hawk*, sailed by Colin Ratsey, came in first, and so won this sweepstake race, which is by way of a preliminary canter to the more important afternoon event, which is a team race for the Island Sailing Club's challenge trophy.

With Stewart Morris teamed up with Peter Scott it looked as though the Oxford and Cambridge Sailing Society would be bound to win this race, for Stewart had won the Prince of Wales' Cup in 1936 and Peter in 1937, so though I had slight concussion from a fall two days earlier, I was most anxious to have a dart at these two. My team mate was Colin Ratsey in *Hawk*, and Norman Moore had kindly lent me his new dinghy *Melita* for the race. If I looked down I felt dizzy, and also if I tacked twice quickly I felt giddy, and so I did not get into the dinghy until just before the five-minute gun, and then sailed sedately to the lee end where I held *Melita* with her sail shaking, so that we had only to haul in our sheets and start when the gun had fired, for I knew I was going to have great difficulty in sailing round the course and could not afford to get into any manoeuvres with another boat. In spite of starting that way I was third at the first mark, but the two boats ahead luffed out into the tide, which let the rest of the fleet up ahead of us, for whereas when I had arrived at the buoy I was third boat, I was now third from last, but on the reach up to Old Castle Point worked up through several boats.

It was a beat back to the finish line, and in order to save tacks I stood out through the Solent until we could lay the line, and in spite of this was fifth boat at the end of the first round. Meanwhile Colin Ratsey in *Hawk* had sailed through into first place, and so the Island Sailing Club boats were first and fifth with the Oxford and Cambridge Sailing Society's boats second and third, Chichester Smith being fourth.

The first five kept their positions on the reach out to the first mark and the run to Old Castle Point, but on the beat to windward home to the finish I sailed past Chichester Smith in *Mirage* and Stewart Morris in *Alarm*, so as Colin had held his lead the Island Sailing Club won this race, for Colin beat Peter over the line and I came over ahead of Stewart and all was well.

The summer season had started and we all felt that the dinghies had a good summer's sport ahead of them.

The last pre-war POW race winner was *Hawk*, the first time since 1931 that Uffa had not designed the winning Fourteen. But *Thunder and Lightning* was pulled out of storage in 1946 and won again with her old owners. This typified how British yachting had stood still in the war years and then continued exactly where it left off — at any rate in design terms. In 1947 Uffa designed and built *Martlet* for Stewart Morris, who won the POW in her in 1947,.1948 and 1949.

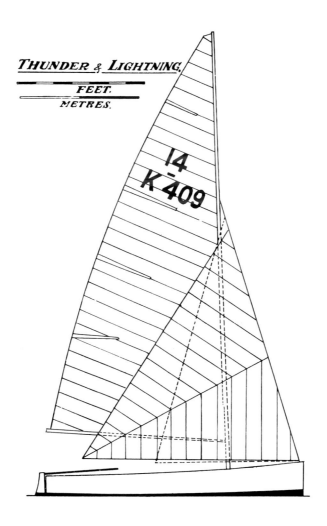

THUNDER & LIGHTNING.
FEET.
METRES.

14
K 409